SOUNDS OF LANGUAGE

readers

Holt, Rinehart and Winston, Inc.
New York, Toronto, London, Sydney

SOUNDS OF LANGUAGE READERS

Sounds

by Bill Martin Jr.
in collaboration with
Peggy Brogan

Freedomring

Acknowledgments

This book is fondly dedicated to Craig T. Senft whose friendship and faith launched the "Sounds of Language"

The Authors and Holt, Rinehart and Winston, Inc., thank the following authors, publishers, agents and parties whose help and permissions to reprint materials have made this book possible. If any errors in acknowledgments have occurred, the errors were inadvertent and will be corrected in subsequent editions as they are realized.

Samuel W. Allen, for permission to reprint his poem, "To Satch." And also for his translation from the French of "They Came That Night," by Leon Damas.

Atheneum Publishers, Inc., for "Schenectady," from CATCH A LITTLE RHYME by Eve Merriam. Copyright © 1966 by Eve Merriam. Used by permission of Atheneum Publishers, Inc.

Blond Educational, Leicester, England, for permission to reprint the poem "Brainstorm" by Adrian Longford (II).

Jonathan Cape, Ltd., for "Blue Butterfly Day," from THE POETRY OF ROBERT FROST. Reprinted by permission.

Jonathan Cape, Ltd., for "Loveliest of Trees," from COLLECTED POEMS, by A. E. Housman. Reprinted by permission.

The Chicago Tribune-New York News Syndicate, Inc., for "BROOM-HILDA" Cartoon on pages 280 and 281. Copyright © 1971. All rights reserved. Reprinted through the courtesy of The Chicago Tribune-New York News Syndicate Inc.

The Christian Science Monitor, for the poems, "Call Me Black," "Lions," and "Love and Wrath," by Brant Shoemaker. Copyright © 1969 by The Christian Science Publishing Society. All rights reserved. Used by permission.

Clara Music Publishers, Inc., for "NOAH," a version of the traditional song by Harry Belefonte and Bill Attaway. Copyright © 1955 by Clara Music Publishers, Inc. All rights reserved. Used by permission.

Thomas Y. Crowell Company, Inc., for "A Road Down in the Sea," by Lorenz Graham. Text Copyright 1946 by Lorenz Graham. Illustrations Copyright © 1970 by Gregorio Prestopino. Reprinted by permission of Thomas Y. Crowell Company, Inc., publisher.

Leon Damas, for permission to reprint his poem, "They Came That Night."

The Dial Press, Inc., for "Ambition," from A BOWL OF BISHOP, by Morris Bishop. Copyright 1954 by Morris Bishop. Originally appeared in *The New Yorker*. Reprinted by permission of The Dial Press.

Doubleday & Company, Inc., for "My Papa's Waltz," from THE COLLECTED POEMS OF THEODORE ROETHKE. Copyright 1942 by Hearst Magazine, Inc. Reprinted by permission of Doubleday & Company, Inc.

Doubleday & Company, Inc., for the drawings which appear on pages 62 to 64, from *Nature and Science* Magazine, May 6, 1968 issue. Copyright © 1968 by The American Museum of Natural History. Reprinted by permission of Doubleday & Company, Inc.

John R. Dunn, for permission to reprint his poems, "Of Geese and Men," "De Hunta," and his story, "The Buck and the Old Man."

Echo Magazine, for their kind permission to use the text and art for "New Portraits in an American Gallery," on pages 328 to 351.

Mary Martin Kreamer, for her kind permission to use the poem which appears on page 151, "Growing Up, Growing Older."

Norma Millay Ellis, for permission to reprint "God's World," by Edna St. Vincent Millay, from COLLECTED POEMS, Harper & Row. Copyright 1917 & 1945 by Edna St. Vincent Millay.

Jay Ells, for permission to use his story and illustrations, "The Boy Who Became a Hotel."

Faber and Faber, Ltd., London, for "My Papa's Waltz," from THE COLLECTED POEMS OF THEODORE ROETHKE. Copyright 1952 by Hearst Magazine, Inc. Used by permission.

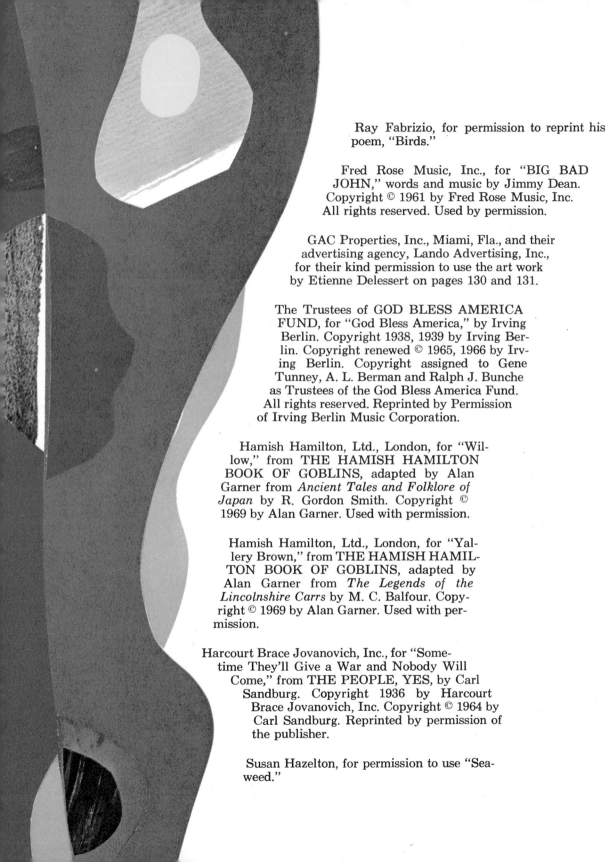

Ronald Himler, for permission to use his poem and illustrations for "Run Gabriella, Run."

Holt, Rinehart and Winston, Inc., for "Blue Butterfly Day," from THE POETRY OF ROBERT FROST, edited by Edward Connery Latham. Copyright 1923 and © 1969 by the publisher. Reprinted by permission of Holt, Rinehart and Winston, Inc.

Holt, Rinehart and Winston, Inc., for "Loveliest of Trees," from THE COLLECTED POEMS OF A. E. HOUSMAN. Copyright 1924 and © 1965 by the publisher. Reprinted by permission of Holt, Rinehart and Winston, Inc.

Indiana University Press, for "Staying Alive," from NEW AND SELECTED POEMS by David Waggoner. Originally appeared in The New Yorker. Copyright © 1965 by David Waggoner. Reprinted by permission of the Indiana University Press.

Indiana University Press, for "Where the Rainbow Ends," by Richard Rive. From POEMS FROM BLACK AFRICA. Reprinted by permission of the Indiana University Press.

JEREMY MUSIC, INC., for the song, "Book Report," words and music by Clark Gesner. From the musical play, YOU'RE A GOOD MAN, CHARLIE BROWN, music and lyrics by Clark Gesner. Copyright © 1967 & 1968 by JEREMY MUSIC, INC. All rights reserved. Reprinted by permission.

Philip Keils, for permission to use his verse, "Ten Billion, Ten Million, Ten Thousand and Ten."

The John Day Company, Inc., for "Funny the Way Different Cars Start," from I LIKE AUTOMOBILES, by Dorothy Baruch. Copyright 1931 and © 1958 by Dorothy Walter Baruch. Reprinted by permission of The John Day Company, Inc.

Alfred A. Knopf, Inc., for "Sonic Boom," from TELEPHONE POLES AND OTHER POEMS, by John Updike. Copyright © 1959 by John Updike, and reprinted by permission of Alfred A. Knopf, Inc.

Alfred A. Knopf, Inc., for "Ties" from THE DIVING BELL, by Dabney Stuart. Copyright © 1966 by Dabney Stuart. Reprinted by permission of Alfred A. Knopf, Inc.

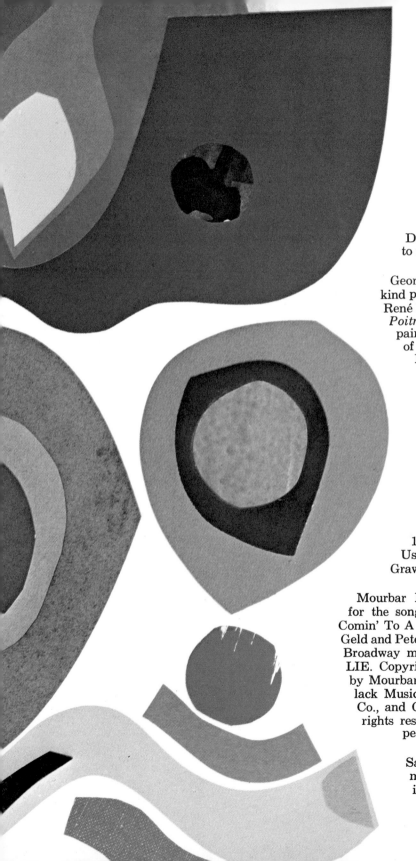

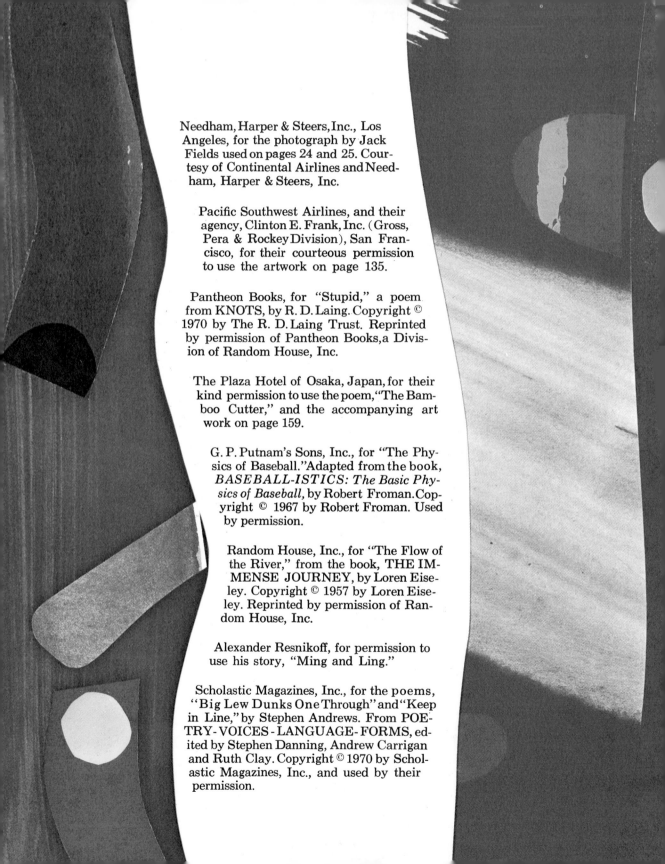

Needham, Harper & Steers, Inc., Los Angeles, for the photograph by Jack Fields used on pages 24 and 25. Courtesy of Continental Airlines and Needham, Harper & Steers, Inc.

Pacific Southwest Airlines, and their agency, Clinton E. Frank, Inc. (Gross, Pera & Rockey Division), San Francisco, for their courteous permission to use the artwork on page 135.

Pantheon Books, for "Stupid," a poem from KNOTS, by R. D. Laing. Copyright © 1970 by The R. D. Laing Trust. Reprinted by permission of Pantheon Books, a Division of Random House, Inc.

The Plaza Hotel of Osaka, Japan, for their kind permission to use the poem, "The Bamboo Cutter," and the accompanying art work on page 159.

G. P. Putnam's Sons, Inc., for "The Physics of Baseball." Adapted from the book, *BASEBALL-ISTICS: The Basic Physics of Baseball,* by Robert Froman. Copyright © 1967 by Robert Froman. Used by permission.

Random House, Inc., for "The Flow of the River," from the book, THE IMMENSE JOURNEY, by Loren Eiseley. Copyright © 1957 by Loren Eiseley. Reprinted by permission of Random House, Inc.

Alexander Resnikoff, for permission to use his story, "Ming and Ling."

Scholastic Magazines, Inc., for the poems, "Big Lew Dunks One Through" and "Keep in Line," by Stephen Andrews. From POETRY-VOICES-LANGUAGE-FORMS, edited by Stephen Danning, Andrew Carrigan and Ruth Clay. Copyright © 1970 by Scholastic Magazines, Inc., and used by their permission.

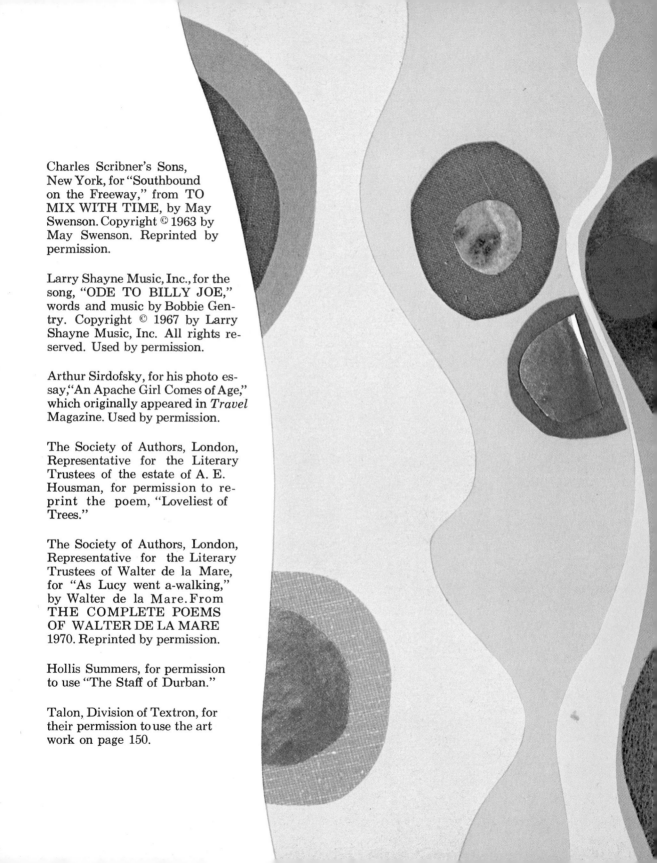

Dawn C. Thomas, for permission to use her story, "The Power of Eye."

United *Feature* Syndicate, Inc., New York, for their courteous permission to reprint the PEANUTS Cartoon on pages 308 and 309. Copyright © 1967 by United *Feature* Syndicate, Inc.

UPI, for permission to use the photograph of the earth on page 384.

Henry Z. Walch, Inc., New York, for "Willow," from A CAVALCADE OF GOBLINS. Adapted by Alan Garner from *Ancient Tales and Folklore of Japan* by R. Gordon Smith. Copyright © 1969 by Alan Garner. Used with permission.

Henry Z. Walch, Inc., New York, for "Yallery Brown," from A CAVALCADE OF GOBLINS. Adapted by Alan Garner from *Legends of the Lincolnshire Carrs* by M. C. Balfour. Copyright © 1969 by Alan Garner. Used with permission.

Joel Weltman, for permission to use his photographs on page 243 through 253.

Ken Williams, for permission to use his story, "The Ghostly Hitchhiker."

Dr. Paul Witty, for his rendering of the essay, "The Theory of Relativity."

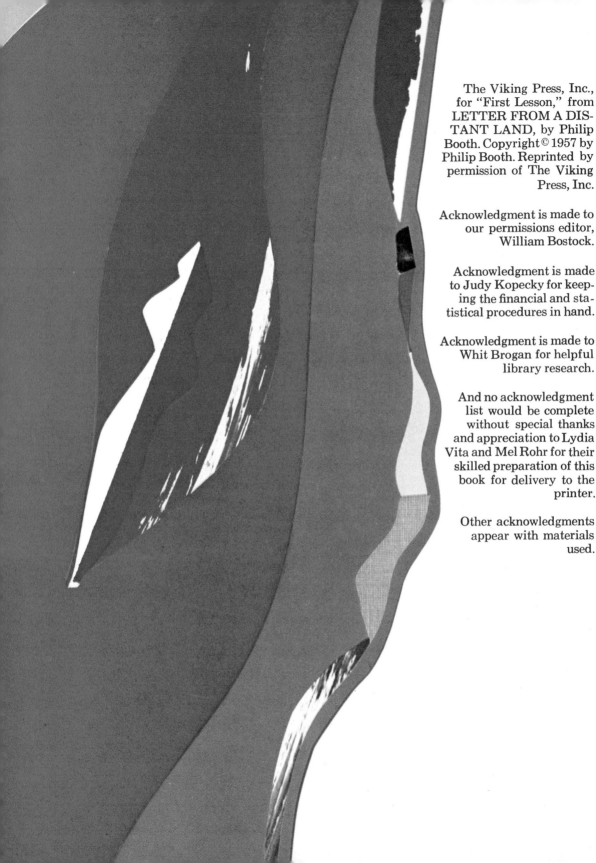

The Viking Press, Inc., for "First Lesson," from LETTER FROM A DISTANT LAND, by Philip Booth. Copyright © 1957 by Philip Booth. Reprinted by permission of The Viking Press, Inc.

Acknowledgment is made to our permissions editor, William Bostock.

Acknowledgment is made to Judy Kopecky for keeping the financial and statistical procedures in hand.

Acknowledgment is made to Whit Brogan for helpful library research.

And no acknowledgment list would be complete without special thanks and appreciation to Lydia Vita and Mel Rohr for their skilled preparation of this book for delivery to the printer.

Other acknowledgments appear with materials used.

Table of Contents

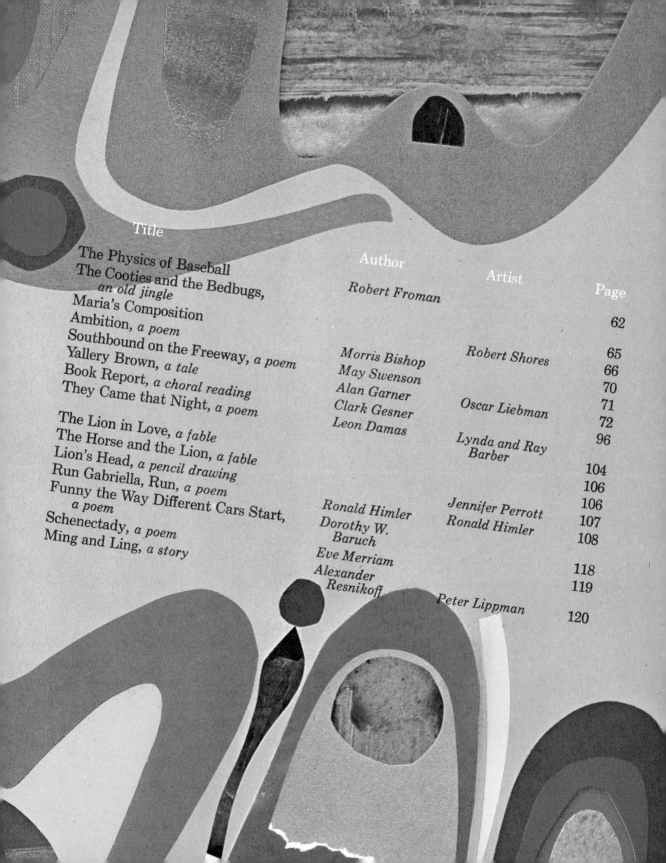

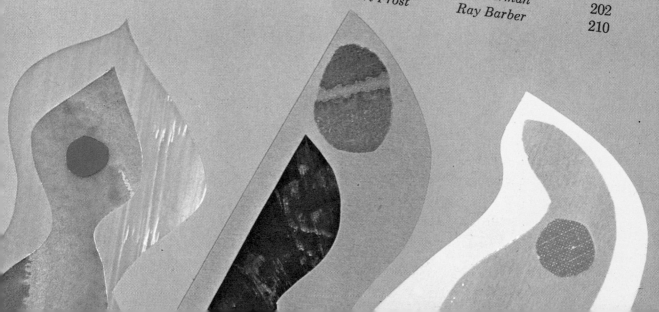

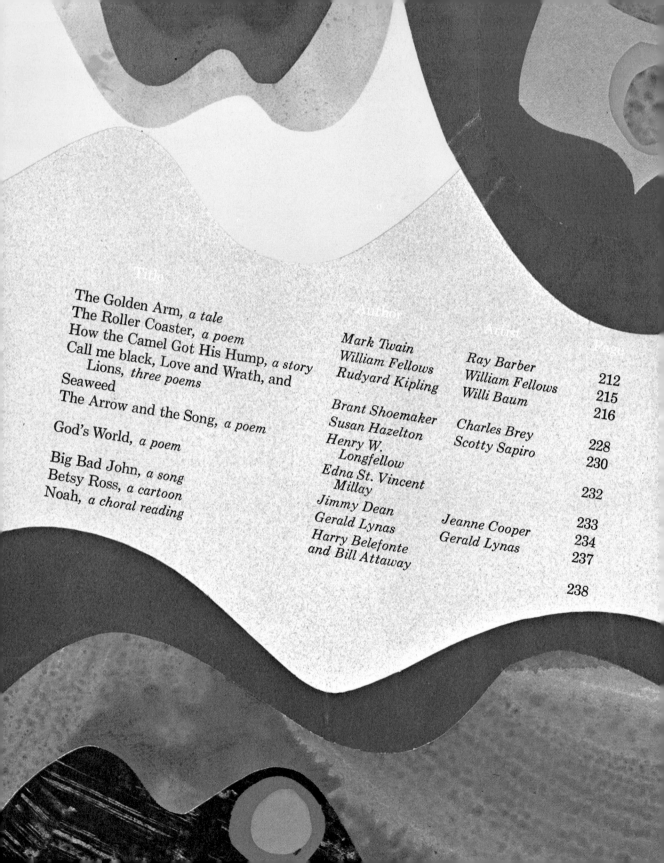

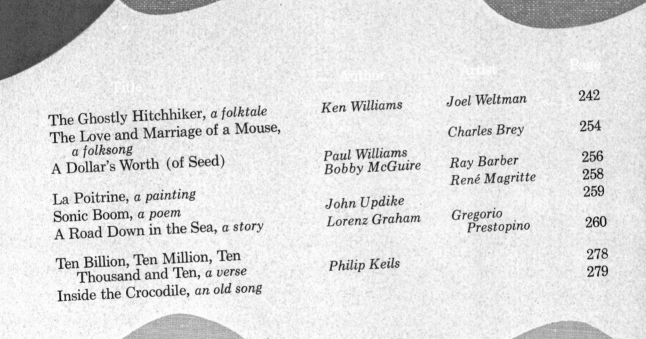

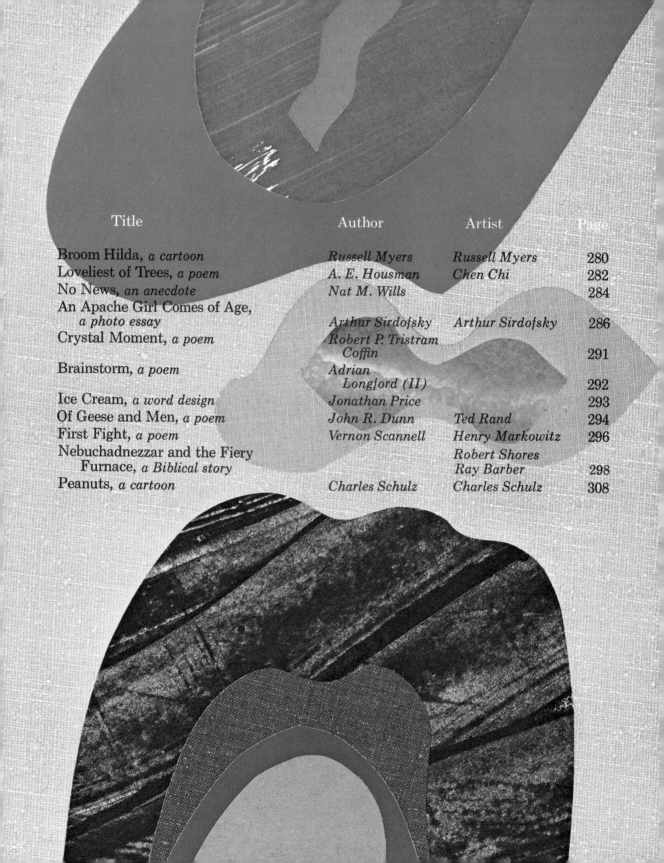

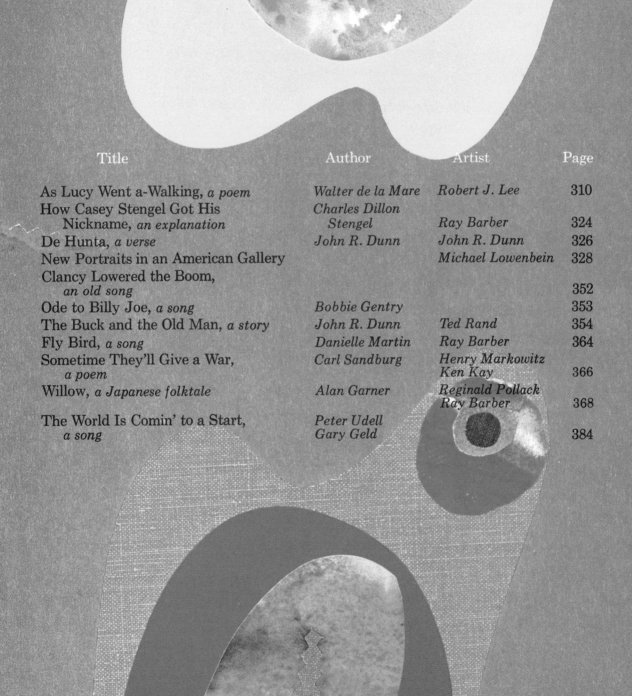

A SONG BY IRVING BERLIN, DESIGN BY RAY BARBER

God bless America,
Land that I Love,
Stand beside her and guide her
Thru the night with a
light from above;
From the mountains,
to the prairies,
To the oceans
white with foam,
God bless America,
My home sweet home.

Where the Rainbow Ends

A POEM BY RICHARD RIVE, PHOTOGRAPH BY JACK FIELDS

Where the rainbow ends
There's going to be a place, brother,
Where the world can sing all sorts of songs,
And we're going to sing together, brother,
You and I, though you're white and I'm not.
It's going to be a sad song, brother,
Because we don't know the tune,
And it's a difficult tune to learn.
But we can learn, brother, you and I.
There's no such tune as a black tune.
There's no such tune as a white tune.
There's only music, brother,
And it's music we're going to sing
Where the rainbow ends.

Ski Country A PICTURE FOR DREAMING BY EDWARD FELLA

Theory of Relativity

AS RECALLED BY DR. PAUL WITTY

Professor Einstein went to a party one night
and the hostess said,
"Professor Einstein will tell us
the meaning of relativity."

"I shall tell you a story instead," he said:

> I was going down the street the other day
> with a blind friend
> and I remarked that I should like a glass of milk.

"What is milk?" asked my blind friend.
"A white liquid," I answered.
"Liquid I know, but what is white?"
"The color of swan's feathers."
"Feathers I know, but what is a swan?"
"A bird with a crooked neck."
"Neck I know, but what is crooked?"
By that time I had grown impatient
and I seized his arm and bent it.
I said, "This is crooked."
Then I straightened his arm and said,
"This is straight."
"Ah," said my blind friend,
"now I know what you mean by milk."

Then Mr. Einstein turned to his hostess and said,
"Would you like me to tell you more
about relativity?"

Di Tri Berrese BY MONKEY BUSINESS

Uans oppona taim ues tre berrese;
mamma berre, pappa berre, a bebi berre.
Live inne contri nire foresta.
NAISE AUS.
NO MUCHEGGIA.
Unno doi, pappa, mamma, e bebi
go tudia bice,
anie furghette loche di dorre.
Bai enne bai commose Goldilocchese,
sci garra nattinghe tu du
batta meiche troble.
Sci puschie olle fudde daon di maute;
no leve cromme.
Dan schi gos appesterese
ene slipse in alle beddse.
LEISE SLOBBE!
Bai anne bai commese omme
di tri berrese,

alle sonnebronde enne sand inna scius.
Dei garra no fudde,
garra no beddse.
En wara dei goine due to Goldilocchese?
Tro erie inne strit?
Colle pullssemenne?
FETTE CIENZE!
Dei uas Italien Berrese,
enne dei slippe onna florre.
Goldilocchese stei derre tree unidase;
itte aute ausenomme;
on guista becose dei asche erra
to meiche di beddse,
sci sai "Go jumpe in di lache,"
enne runne omma criane
to erre mamma
tellen erre uat sanigunses
di tri berres uor.
Uatsiuse? Uara ju goine du?
—Go compliene sittiole?

The Boy

Who

Became a Hotel

by Jay Ells

On a clear sunny morning at the edge of the forest Sam swang from the vines of morning glories.

He crouched and looked at a flower. Taking it to his nose he said, "I love your smell." Touching it to his cheek he said, "I love your soft petals." Putting it under his eye he said, "I love your yellow color."

The flower opened as far as it could, breathed out its most delicious perfume, raised its most velvety fibers and blushed its most golden yellow. "Mmmmmmmmmm," it said in a low hum.

A lady bug resting in the flower looked up and

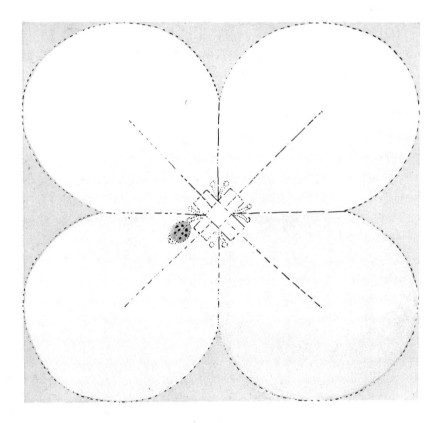

saw the boy's eye looking into the flower. She said,

"I love you, Eye. You can see. You see this flower and it becomes more beautiful. Follow me, Eye, into the forest.

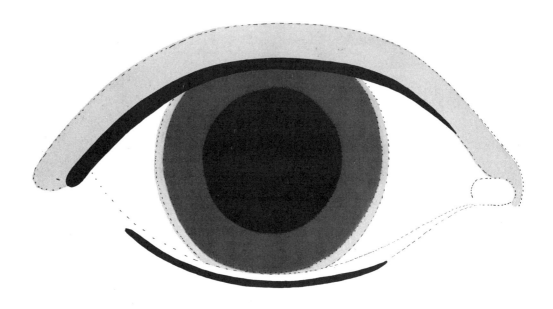

Follow me into the forest and see every flower and you will make every flower in the forest more beautiful."

Sam looked up and saw a wolf. He looked into
the wolf's eyes. The wolf returned the gaze. The wolf
had seen the boy at the flower and had crept close
saying to himself, "That boy knows something."

The boy waited and breathed deeply. He felt
friendship toward the wolf. He felt the wolf wanted
to talk to him.

The wolf snapped involuntarily. Why was the boy
so quiet? The wolf sprang at the boy—then passed
quickly—the wolf's fur brushing the boy's arm.
The wolf disappeared into the forest.

Sam followed the lady bug into the forest.
They passed:

Bunnies + Flowers

wild pigs

toads + lillies

a pond with fish

temples & monuments.

He didn't see the lady bug anymore.
He heard an animal crying.

Just off the path he found a bear caught in a trap.
He opened the jaws of the trap and freed the bear's
hurt foot. Pain from the foot filled the bear's eyes.
The bear grabbed the boy.

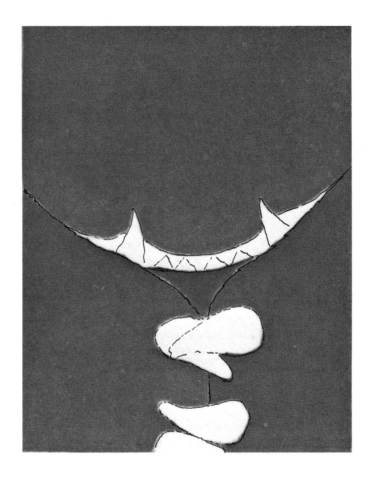

The boy heard the heartbeat of the bear and
struggled against the warm embrace. The bear bit the
boy on the shoulder and again on the middle of
the body. The boy struggled against the bear and/ the

It was night when he awoke.
He felt for his wounds. They were healed.
He was in a jungle.
He looked up at the moon.
He saw a large bird in the sky.
He cried out, "Big Bird, come down."
And the bird flew down and said, "What do you want?"

"Take me to the moon," said the boy. He put his arm around the bird's neck. He swung his leg over the bird's back. The bird took the boy to the moon.

"I love you, Moon," he said. He pressed his face close to the moon.

The moon beamed, "I shine for you, Sam."

"Take me back to the jungle, Big Bird," said the boy. And the bird took the boy back to the jungle.

A tiger came through the jungle on his soft feet. The tiger put his head in front of the boy and looked him in the eye. Sam put his arm around the tiger and said, "You're beautiful, Tiger. Will you be my friend?"

The tiger purred softly. The tiger rubbed his nose on the boy's nose. "Ride on my back. I will take you deep into the jungle."

The boy rode on the tiger's back. Deep in the
jungle's heart they stopped at the tiger's den.

The tiger said, "Give me your arms. My children are hungry." The boy bent down and the tiger cubs ate his arms. The boy grew four new arms. The tigers left the boy.

The boy stood very still. A bird rested on each of his arms. "Give us your hair," said the birds. "We need it to build our nests."

"Take what you need," said the boy. The birds took his hair. In its place grew flames. "We will use your hair to build nests for our young," said the birds. "In its place we leave fire, and you will not be burned, but will be a light for everyone."

The animals and birds and butterflies stood in the jungle enchanted by the shining boy. The python crawled over the boy's legs, coiled himself around the boy's body, and hugged the boy tightly. He looked into the boy's face. His eyes glittered. His fangs stuck out and his tongue went back and forth. The boy's cheek touched the tongue of the snake. "I love you, Snake," the boy said.

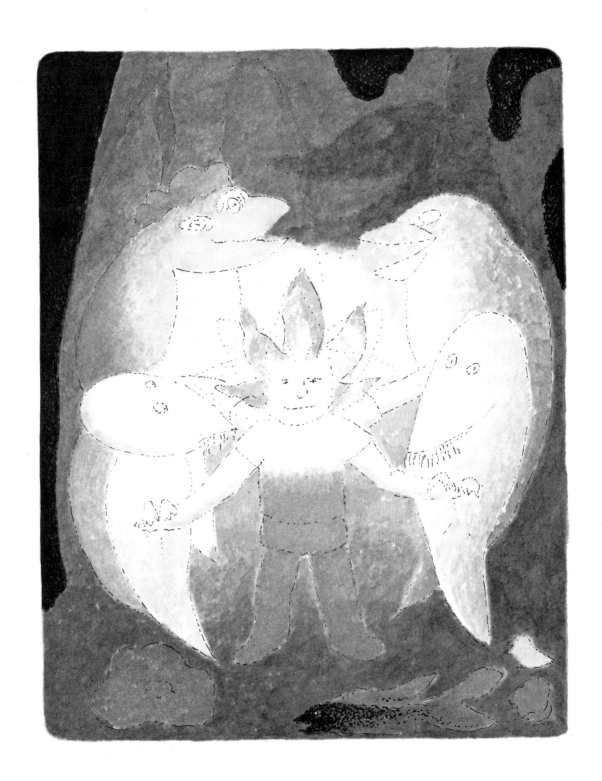

The snake said, "I am hungry. Give me your head."
"Take my head, Snake."

The snake opened his mouth and ate the boy's head. The snake said, "You have seen me for what I am. You have seen all of life in me. The same life that you have known in yourself you have seen in me. You have seen that. No one else has seen so much. You have loved all life without separation. You have seen all ways at once."

The boy grew a new head which had four faces— one on each side.

"I can see," he said and he sat down.

He became very large until he was so large

that he was a shelter for all of the animals in the jungle.
His skin became like stone. He did not move and
he saw everything.

And the fire on his head made clouds which
floated over the world.

From the clouds came rain which said to the earth,
"I love you."

And the earth gave flowers to the rain and to the
sun and to all of the animals.

And the animals brought the flowers to the boy
in the jungle.

Catching a Thief folklore

One time
dark overtook an old preacher
and no way he could do
but try the next house he 'uld come to
and see would they let him
stay the night there.
So at the next house 'side the road,
he went and knocked.
And they said Yes, he could stay.

So they cooked him something to eat,
and after he'd sat by the fire
and talked with 'em a while,
he went on in the next room
where they'd fixed him a bed.
Laid down and went off to sleep.

Well these folks were pretty rough,
and some more came there
and they were all drinkin' and gamblin'
and one-thing-and-another,
till a big argument started.
Seemed some money was missing.
The man of the house
he tried to make 'em hush.
Says, "There's a preacher asleep in yonder."
But they kept right on hollerin'
and a fight was about to start.

Well that preacher had woke up
and he lay there listenin'
to what-'n-all they were arguin' so loud over.
And he got up,
pulled on his clothes,
and went in amongst 'em.

They sort of quieted down then,
and he got to talkin' with some of 'em:
told that he could find out which one it was
had played the rogue.

Then they all got right still
and listened to him.
"Get me a rooster," he told 'em.

Somebody went out and reached up in the tree
where the chickens were roostin',
and brought him the rooster.
Then he went and locked all the doors,
and put the keys in his pocket.
"Now," he says,
"I'll get a pot."
And he reached down
and got hold of a big pot
there at the fireplace.

"Blow out the lights," he says,
"and cover the fire."
So they did that.

"Now," he told 'em,
"I'm going to put the rooster under this pot,
and I'll stand right here;
and if everybody will come
and draw his hand across the pot,
when the rogue does that the rooster will crow,
and right then whoever it is
I'll grab him for ye."

There was a lot of shufflin' around in the dark
and the old preacher kept sayin',
"Now the next 'un.
Let somebody else
come on and rub the pot."
And finally everything got quiet again.

"Anybody else?—
Well, if any man or woman hasn't had his go
just speak up."

Nobody spoke.
And the old rooster
hadn't let out a single squawk.

"Uh-oh! I reckon I've made a failure.
Light the lights."

They lit the lamps and candles again
and got the fire goin' bright once more.
Then the preacher spoke up, says,
"Gather around a minute here—
all of ye."

They circled up around him.

"Hold out your hands, now!
—all of ye!"

And there was only one man
whose hands were not black from the soot
on the bottom of that pot.

The old preacher pointed at him, says,
"You give back that money, sir!"

60

Short History of Man

A POEM BY JOHN HOLMES

Quick! Grab the baby, the precious pet.
He'll pitch right out of his bassinet.
Hey! Raise the side of the fellow's crib.
He's getting over. He'll crack a rib.
Look out! Today is the day he dares
Climb the gate at the top of the stairs.
Go get him! He's out in the entrance-hall.
I thought his play-pen looked too small.
Hurry up there! Fence the garden in
As high as a very tall man's chin.
Come on! He's learned to lift the latch,
And I have an idea he's hard to catch.
Run! Run faster! We're still too slow.
What do you say if we let him go?

61

THE PHYSICS OF BASEBALL

When you go to a baseball game, you probably take along such things as pennants, candy bars, and a few friends. Chances are that a physical scientist going to a ball game would take along much the same kinds of things. But if the physicist wanted to, he could bring along pencil, paper, and slide rule, and tell you quite a few things about the game that neither you nor the players probably knew before.

What the physicist could tell you is how physical "laws" help determine what happens on the ball field. Regardless of who the players are or which team he wants to win, the physicist knows that certain things must happen whenever a ball is hit, thrown, or caught, or whenever a player is moving on the field.

This doesn't mean that you have to know physics to play baseball well, or that a physicist could play baseball any better than someone else. But knowing a little more about how things happen during the game probably helps the physicist to enjoy it a little more. Maybe these examples of the physics of baseball will help you to enjoy the game a little more, too

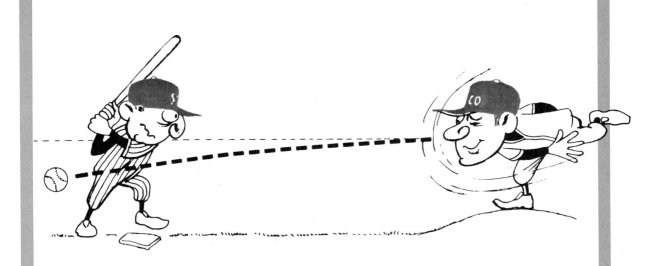

As soon as a baseball leaves the pitcher's hand, gravity begins pulling it downward. Even a fast ball will drop about 2½ feet by the time it reaches the batter. That's why the pitcher's mound is built up 15 inches higher than home plate, and why a good pitcher always aims the ball a little higher than where he actually wants it to cross the plate. (In a softball game, should the pitcher's mound be higher than home plate? Why?)

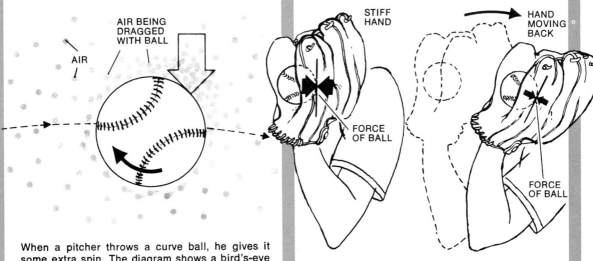

When a pitcher throws a curve ball, he gives it some extra spin. The diagram shows a bird's-eye view of the spinning ball and the surrounding air. The surface of the spinning ball drags a little air around with it, and the air that it drags forward on one side of the ball piles into the air just ahead of the ball (see diagram). This pile-up of air tends to push the ball away, toward the side of the ball where the air is being dragged backward instead of forward.

Watch the shortstop catch a line drive, and see how his arm moves back a little with the ball. If the ball is hit very hard, his whole body may move back a little. Letting his arm or body "give" spreads the force of the ball striking the shortstop's glove over a longer time, and over a greater mass (his whole arm or body) than stopping the ball with a stiff hand would. So his hand feels less shock.

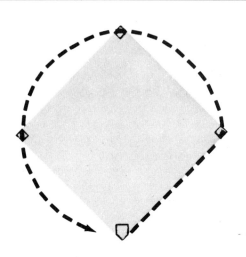

Sportscasters talk about a runner's "rounding" the bases because that's just what he does. *Inertia* tends to make a moving object keep going in a straight line. In order to make a sharp turn at each base, a runner would have to stop, turn, then start again. There's no time for that, so the runner follows a curved path around the base while keeping most of his speed.

When a runner slides into second base, do you think he's doing it so he can get to the base faster? Sliding may help him to avoid being tagged by the second baseman, but its main purpose is usually to slow the runner down. The runner uses *friction* between the ground and his clothes or body to reduce his speed and help keep him from going past the base.

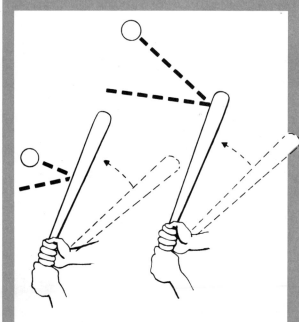

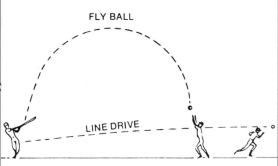

FLY BALL

LINE DRIVE

If a batter hits a ball squarely near the heavy end of his bat, the ball will fly off faster than if it is hit squarely at the middle of the bat. Can you figure out why?

A fly ball is usually easier to catch than a line drive. A lot of the energy given to a fly ball by the bat is used up in making the ball go high into the air against the force of gravity. So the ball doesn't travel as fast or as far from the plate as a line drive hit with the same force. By the time the ball comes down, the outfielder may be waiting for it.

```
                    W
                  HEN I
                WOKE UP TH
              IS MORNING THE
            RE UPON THE WALL T
          HE COOTIES AND THE BEDB
        UGS WERE HAVING A GAME OF B
          ALL THE SCORE WAS 6-0 THE C
            OOTIES WERE AHEAD TH
              EN THE BEDBUGS
                GOTTA HOME
                  RUN AN
              o                 k
            u                    n
          t                       o
                      D            c
                                    k
        f o                         e
                                     d
      b                               m
    e                                  e
  d

  .
```

Maria's Composition

Maria is a 13 year old Puerto Rican girl
in an East Harlem Junior High School.
Her story is printed here,
with all its errors and innocence,
just as she wrote it.

"Stop don't do it"
"Please stop them"
"Help" she screamed.

That was the words she prenounce
when I was coming from the store.
When I was coming up the stairs
I saw blood down the stair
and I look up I saw three policeman
and two detective
and I said what's wrong,
were does blood come from?
The detective said in a deep voice
this blood come from the second floor
two neighbors had a fight,
and we are waiting for the ambulance.
My heart stop for one second,
and then I ran up the stairs and I said.
"That is where I live."
When I came up and saw Mr. Lopez
with blood all over his shirt
and I kneel down and said
"Mr. Lopez what happen"
and he said "That no good Luis he"
he stop and then I said go on,
but the policeman interb and said
please goung girl
don't try to make him talk,

Painting by Robert Shores

then a policeman and a fat lady
the lady was the nurse and she said
take this man immediately!
to the ambulance he is bleeding to much.
The policeman took him to the ambulance.
The other she put some bandage around his shoulders
and then she said go to your home
and report tomorrow at the hospital.
Then the nurse call me over and said
do you know the man that I sent in the ambulance?
Yes nurse.
"Then will you answer some questions."
Yes.
Will you please companion me to the hospital.
Yes nurse.
Mr. Lopez die in the ambulance,
I call Mrs. Lopez and gave her the bad news.
She started to scream and cry.
I came back from the hospital
after I answer the question.
The first thing that came in my mine was "why" "why"
two neighbors fight.
"Why" because they maybe don't understand each other
or maybe one ask for a advice and the other said
why come to me why don't you go to your family.

To a neighbor is not necessary to be in the neighborhood,
it can be country or city or town anything.

For example if you go to a country
that you never gone before.
All during your travels
you would see people staring at your odd clothing,
people who would not understand the language you spoke.

Then you would land in a strange country.
Everything would be different.
You would have to learn a strange language,
learn a new trade.
Then you try to be kindful and helpful with people.
The people will adore you truly.
"Why" because you been not only a good neighbor
but helpful and friendly with them.
This is one of the simple ways to be kind with people,
by helping them in anything they need
your help today and tomorrow they help you.
This composition is for the adolescent
to give them an ideal to understand other persons.
When a boy or girl comes into a classroom for the first time
you try to make a conversation with him or her.
Show the boy or girl around the school
introduct the boy or girl
to your friends
so she don't feel lonely.
In a way you are helping the boy or girl getting around.

(NOTE: At the end of this composition, the teacher had written: "too long!")

Ambition

A POEM BY MORRIS BISHOP

I got pocketed behind 7X-3824;
He was making 65, but I can do a little more.
I crowded him on the curves, but I couldn't
    get past,
And on the straightaways there was always
    some truck coming fast.
Then we got to the top of a mile-long incline
And I edged her out to the left, a little
    over the white line,
And ahead was a long grade with construction
    at the bottom,
And I said to the wife, "Now by golly I got'm!"
I bet I did 85 going down the long grade,
And I braked her down hard in front of the
    barricade,
And swung in ahead of him and landed fine
Behind 9W-7679.

Southbound on the Freeway

A POEM BY MAY SWENSON

A tourist came in from Orbitville,
parked in the air, and said:
The creatures of this star
are made of metal and glass.
Through the transparent parts
you can see their guts.
Their feet are round and roll
on diagrams or long
measuring tapes, dark
with white lines.
They have four eyes.
The two in back are red.
Sometimes you can see a five-eyed
one, with a red eye turning
on the top of his head.
He must be special —
the others respect him
and go slow
when he passes, winding
among them from behind.
They all hiss as they glide,
like inches, down the marked
tapes. Those soft shapes,
shadowy inside
the hard bodies — are they
their guts or their brains?

I've heard tell
as how the bogles and boggarts
were main bad in the old times,
but I can't rightly say
as I ever saw any of them myself;
not rightly bogles, that is,
but I'll tell you about Yallery Brown.
If he wasn't a boggart,
he was main near it,
and I knew him myself.
So it's all true—
strange and true I tell you.

72

Gown

AN OLD TALE,
ADAPTED BY ALAN GARNER,
ILLUSTRATIONS BY OSCAR LIEBMAN

I was working on the High Farm to them,
and nobbut a lad of sixteen
or maybe eighteen years;
and my mother and folks dwelt
down by the pond yonder,
at the far end of the village.

I had the stables and such to see to,
and the horses to help with,
and odd jobs to do,
and the work was hard,
but the pay good.
I reckon I was an idle scamp,
for I couldn't abide hard work,
and I looked forward all the week to Sundays,
when I'd walk down home,
and not go back till darklins.

By the green lane
I could get to the farm in a matter of twenty minutes,
but there used to be a path
across the west field yonder,
by the side of the spinney,
and on past the fox cover
and so to the ramper,
and I used to go that way.
It was longer for one thing,
and I wasn't never in a hurry to get back to the work,
and it was still and pleasant
like of Summer nights,
out in the broad silent fields,
mid the smell of the growing things.

Folk said as the spinney was haunted,
and for sure I have seen
lots of fairy stones and rings and that,
along the grass edge;
but I never saw nowt
in the way of horrors and boggarts,
let alone Yallery Brown,
as I said before.

One Sunday,
I was walking across the west field.
It was a beautiful July night,
warm and still,
and the air was full of little sounds,
as if the trees and grass
were chattering to their selves.
And all to once
there came a bit ahead of me
the pitifullest greetin I've ever heard,
so, sobbing,
like a bairn spent with fear,
and near heart-broken; breaking off into a moan,
and then rising again
in a long, whimpering wailing
that made me feel sick
nobbut to hark to it.
I was always fond of babbies, too,
and I began to look everywhere
for the poor creature.

"Must be Sally Bratton's,"
I though to myself.
"She was always a flighty thing,
and never looked after it. Like as not,
she's flaunting about the lanes,
and has clean forgot the babby."
But though I looked and looked
I could find nowt.
Nonetheless the sobbing was at my very ear,
so tired like and sorrowful
that I kept crying out,
"Whisht, bairn, whisht!
I'll take you back to your mother
if you'll only hush your greetin."
But for all my looking
I could find nowt.

I keek it under the hedge by
the spinney side,
and I clumb over it,
and I sought up and down by,
and mid the trees,
and through the long grass and weeds,
but I only frightened some sleeping birds,
and stinged my own hands with the nettles.
and I fair gave up to last: I found nowt,
so I stood there,
scratching my head,
and clean beat with it all.
And presently the whimpering got louder and stronger
in the quietness, and I though I could make out words
of some sort.
I harkened with all my ears,
and the sorry thing was saying
all mixed up with sobbing: "O, oh! The stone, the great big stone!
O, oh!
The stone on top!"

Naturally I wondered
where the stone might be,
and I looked again,
and there by the hedge bottom
was a great flat stone,
near buried in the mools,
and hid in the cotted grass and weeds.
One of those stones
as were used to call the Strangers' Tables.
The Strangers danced on them at moonlight nights,
and so they were never meddled with.
It's ill luck, you know,
to cross the Tiddy People.

However, down I fell on my knee-bones by the stone,
and harkened again.
Clearer nor ever,
but tired and spent with greetin
came the little sobbing voice.

"Ooh! Ooh!
The stone, the stone on top."

I was misliking to meddle
with the thing,
but I couldn't stand the whimpering babby,
and I tore like mad at the stone,
till I felt it lifting from the mools,
and all to once
it came with a sigh,
out of the damp earth
and the tangled grass and growing things.
And there, in the hole,
lay a tiddy thing on its back,
blinking up at the moon and at me.

It was no bigger
than a year-old brat,
but it had long cotted hair and beard,
twisted round and round its body,
so as I couldn't see its clouts.
And the hair was all yaller and shining
and silky, like a bairn's; but the face of it was old,
and as if it were hundreds of years
since it was young and smooth.
Just a heap of wrinkles,
and two bright black eyes in the mid,
set in a lot of shining yaller hair;
and the skin was the colour
of the fresh turned earth
in the Spring—
brown as brown could be,
and its bare hands and feet
were brown

like the face of it.
The greetin' had stopped,
but the tears were standing on its cheek,
and the tiddy thing looked mazed like
in the moonshine and the night air.
It was wondering what I'd do, but by
and by it scrambled out of the hole,
and stood looking about it,
and at myself.
It wasn't up to my knee,
but it was the queerest creature
I ever set eyes on.
Brown and yaller all over;
yaller and brown,
as I told you before,
and with such a glint in its eyes,
and such a wizened face,
that I felt feared on it,
for all that it was
so tiddy and old.

The creature's eyes
got some used to the moonlight,
and presently it looked up in my face
as bold as ever was.

"Tom," it says,
"you're a good lad."

As cool as you can think,
it says,
"Tom,
you're a good lad,"
and its voice was soft and high and piping
like a little bird twittering.

I touched my hat,
and began to think what I had ought to say;
but I was clemmed with fright,
and I couldn't open my bog.

"Houts!" says the thing again.
"You needn't be feared of me;
you've done me a better turn than you know,
my lad,
and I'll do as much for you."

I couldn't speak yet,
but I thought:
"Lord!
For sure it's a bogle!"

"No!" it says,
quick as quick,
"I'm not a bogle,
but you'd best not ask me
what I am;
anyways,
I'm a good friend of yours."

My very knee-bones struck,
for certainly an ordinary body
couldn't have known
what I'd been thinking to myself,
but it looked so kind like,
and spoke so fair,
that I made bold to get out,
a bit quavery like:

"Might I be asking to know your honour's name?"

"Hm," it says,
 pulling its beard,
"as for that,"
 and it thought a bit,
"ay so,"
 it went on at last,
"Yallery Brown you may call me;
 Yallery Brown.
 It's my nature, you see.
 And as for a name,
 it will do as well as any other.
 Yallery Brown, Tom,
 Yallery Brown's your friend,
 my lad."

"Thank you, master," says I,
 quite meek like.

"And now," he says,
"I'm in a hurry tonight,
 but tell me quick,
 what shall I do for you?
 Will you have a wife?
 I can give you
 the rampingest lass in the town.
 Will you be rich?
 I'll give you gold
 as much as you can carry.
 Or will you have help with your work?
 Only say the word."

I scratched my head.
'Well, as for a wife,
 I have no hankering after such.
 They're but bothersome bodies,
 and I have women folk to home
 as will mend my clouts.
 And for gold;
 that's as may be," for, you see,
 I thought he was talking only,
 and may be he couldn't do
 as much as he said,
"but as for work—
 there, I can't abide work,
 and if you'll give me
 a helping hand in it, I'll thank you."

"Stop," says he,
 quick as lightning.
"I'll help you, and welcome,
 but if ever you say that to me—
 if ever you thank me, do you see?—
 you'll never see me more.
 Mind that now.
 I want no thanks,
 I'll have no thanks,
 do you hear?"
 And he stamped his tiddy foot
 on the earth
 and looked
 as wicked as a raging bull.
 But when I went to the work,
 there was none to do!
 All was done already!
 The horses seen to,
 the stables cleaned out,
 everything in its proper place,
 and I'd nowt to do
 but sit with my hands in my pockets.

And so it went on day after day,
all the work done by Yallery Brown,
and better done, too,
than I could have done it myself.
And if the master gave me more work,
    I sat down by, and the work
                    did itself,
                    the singeing irons,
                    or the besom,
                    or what not, set to,
                            and with never a hand
                            put to them
                        would get through in no time.
                    For I never saw Yallery Brown
                    in daylight; only in the darklins
                    I have seen him bopping about,
                    like a will-o-the-wyke.
            "Mind that now,
             great lump as you be,"
             he went on,
             calming down a bit,
          "and if ever you need help,
             or get into trouble,
             call on me and just say,
             'Yallery Brown, come from the mools,
             I want thee!'
             and I shall be with you to once.
             And now," says he,
             picking up a dandelion puff,
          "good night to you."
             And he blowed it up,
             and it all came in my eyes and ears.

84

Soon as I could see again,
  the tiddy creature was gone,
    and but for the stone on end,
  and the hold at my feet,
  I'd have thought I'd been dreaming.

Well, I went home and to bed,
and by the morning I'd near forgot all about it.
  without his lanthorn.

To first, it was mighty fine for me.
I'd nowt to do, and good pay for it;
  but by and by,
  things began to go arsy-varsy.
If the work was done for me,
  it was undone for the other lads.
If my buckets were filled,
  theirs were upset.
If my tools were sharpened,
  theirs were blunted and spoiled.
If my horses were clean as daisies,
  theirs were splashed with muck.
  And so on.
  Day in, day out,
  it was always the same.
And the lads saw Yallery Brown
  flitting about of nights,
and they saw the things working
  without hands of days,
and they saw as my work was done for me,
  and theirs undone for them,
    and naturally they began to look shy on me,
    and they wouldn't speak or come near me,
      and they carried tales to the master,
    and so things went from bad to worse.

For — do you see? —
I could do nothing myself.
The brooms wouldn't stay in my hand,
the plough ran away from me,
the hoe kept out of my grip.
I'd thought oft
as I'd do my own work after all,
so as may be Yallery Brown
would leave me
and my neighbours alone.
But I couldn't.
I could only sit by and look on,
and have the cold shoulder turned on me,
whiles the unnatural thing
was meddling with the others,
and working for me.

To last,
    things got so bad
that the master gave me the sack,
        and if he hadn't,
I do believe as all the rest of the lads
        would have sacked him,
    for they swore as they'd not stay
            on the same garth with me.
    Well, naturally I felt bad.
    It was a main good place,
                and good pay, too;
    and I was fair mad with Yallery Brown,
    as had got me into such a trouble.
        So before I knew,
    I shook my fist in the air
and called out as loud as I could:

"Yallery Brown,
        come from the mools;
        thou scamp,
        I want thee!"

You'll scarce believe it,
but I'd hardly brung out the words
as I felt something tweaking my leg behind,
while I jumped with the smart of it.

And soon as I looked down,
there was the tiddy thing,
with his shining hair, and wrinkled face,
and wicked, glinting black eyes.

I was in a fine rage,
and should liked to have kicked him,
but it was no good,
there wasn't enough of him
to get my boot against.

But I said to once: "Look here, master,
I'll thank you to leave me alone after this,
do you hear?
I want none of your help,
and I'll have nowt more to do with you —
see now."

The horrid thing brak out with a screeching laugh,
and pointed his brown finger at me.

"Ho ho, Tom!" says he.
"You've thanked me, my lad,
and I told you not, I told you not!"

"I don't want your help, I tell you!"
I yelled at him.
"I only want never to see you again,
   and to have nowt more
   to do with you.

      You

         can

            go!"

The thing only laughed and screeched and mocked,
         as long as I went on swearing,
            but so soon as my breath gave out,
            "Tom, my lad," he says, with a grin,
               "I'll tell you the summat, Tom.
                  True's true I'll never help you again,
               and call as you will,
                  you'll never see me after today;
                     but I never said as I'll leave you alone, Tom,
                  and I never will, my lad!

            I was nice and safe under the stone, Tom,
               and could do no harm;
                  but you let me out yourself,
                  and you can't put me back again!
            I would have been your friend
            and worked for you if you had been wise,
               but since you are no more than a born fool,
               I'll give you no more than a born fool's luck;
                  and when all goes arsy-varsy,
                  and everything a gee —
                     you'll mind as it's Yallery Brown's doing,
               though happen you didn't see him.
                  Mark my words, will you?"

And he began to sing, dancing round me,
like a bairn with his yaller hair,
but looking older nor ever
    with his grinning wrinkled bit of a face!

"Work as you will,

"You'll never do well, "Work as you might,
    "You'll never gain owt:
"For harm and mischief and Yallery Brown
"You've let out yourself from under the stone."

Ay!
He said those very words,
and they have ringed in my ears ever since,
over and over again,
like a bell tolling for the burying.
And it was the burying of my luck —
for I never had any since.
However, the imp stood there
mocking and grinning at me,
and chuckling like the old devil's
own wicked self.

And man! —
    I can't rightly mind
      what he said next.
      It was all cussing and swearing
     and calling down misfortune on me;
     but I was so mazed in fright
    that I could only stand there,
  shaking all over me,
  and staring down at the horrid thing;
  and I reckon if he'd gone on long,
  I'd have tumbled down in a fit.
  But by and by, his yaller shining hair —
  I can't abide yaller hair since that —
   rose up in the air,
   and wrapped itself round him,
   while he looked for all the world
   like a great dandelion puff;
   and he floated away on the wind
   over the wall and out of sight,
  with a parting skirl of his wicked voice
  and sneering laugh.

  I tell you,
   I was near dead with fear,
   and I can't scarcely tell
  how I ever got home at all,
but I did somehow, I suppose.

Well, that's all;
it's not much of a tale,
but it's true,
every word of it;
and there's others besides me
as have seen Yallery Brown
and known his evil tricks —
and did it come true, you say?
But it did sure!
I have worked here and there,
and turned my hand to this and that,
but it always went a gee,
and it is all Yallery Brown's doing.
The children died, and my wife didn't;
the beasts never fatted,
and nothing ever did well with me.
I'm going old now, and I shall must end
my days in the house. I reckon;
but till I'm dead and buried,
and happen even afterwards,
there'll be no end to Yallery Brown's spite at me.
And day in and day out I hear him saying,
whiles I sit here trembling:

"Work as you will,
"You'll never do well;
"Work as you might,
"You'll never gain owt;
"For harm

and mischief
and Yallery Brown
"You've let out yourself
from under the stone."

95

This is a "Charlie Brown" choral reading. The color coding cues each of the characters when to read. Many times the four are reading simultaneously but each saying something different. It's pure fun!

BOOK REPORT
WORDS AND MUSIC BY CLARK GESNER

All: "Homework, yech!"

Linus: A Book Re – port on Pe – ter

Lucy: A Book Re – port on Pe – ter Rab – bit Pe – ter

Schroeder: A

Rab – bit, Pe – ter ___ Rab bit ___ Rab –

Rab – bit, Pe – ter Rab – bit ___ Rab –

Book Re – port on Pe – ter Rab – bit.

Charlie Brown: A Book Re – port on Pe – ter

Rab – bit.

Rab – bit. Pe – ter Rab – bit is this stu – pid book

Rab – Rab – bit.

a – bout this stu – pid rab – bit who steals veg – 'ta – bles

from oth – er peo – ple's gar – dens. 1, 2, 3, 4, 5, 6, 7, 8, 9, 10,

11, 12, 13, 14, 15, 16, 17. Hum, 83 to go

Schroeder: The name of the book a-bout which, This Book

Re – port is a – bout is Pe – ter Rab – bit ___ which

96

is   a –   bout this   rab – bit.   I   found   it

ver – y....   I   liked   the   part where....

It   was   a....   It   re – mind – ed   me   of   Rob – in Hood.

And the   part where Lit – tle John   jumped from   a   rock   to   the

Sher – iff   of   Not – ting – ham's   back,   And then   Rob – in

and ev – 'ry – one   swung from   the   trees in   a   sud – den   sur –

prise____   at – tack,   And   they cap-tured the Sher – iff and   all

of   his goods and they car – ried him back to their camp in   the woods,

and the Sher – iff was guest at   their   din – ner and all,   But   he

wrig – gled   a – way and   he   sound – ed   the   call,   and his men

rushed in   and the ar – rows flew... Pe – ter Rab – bit did sort of

97

that   kind   of   thing,   too.

              Lucy: The   oth – er   peo – ple's   name   was   Mac –

Gre   –   gor.   18, 19, 20, 21, 22, 23.

                           Linus: In examining a work such as Peter

Rabbit, it is important that the superficial characteristics of its deceptively simple plot

should not be allowed to blind the reader to the more substantial fabric of its deeper

motivations.

          In this report I plan to discuss the sociological implications of family

pressures so great as to drive an otherwise moral rabbit to perform acts of thievery . . .

. . . which he consciously knew were against the law. I also hope to explore the person-

ality of Mr. MacGregor in his conflicting roles as farmer and humanitarian. Peter

Rabbit is established from the start as a benevolent

98

hero. It is only with the increase of social....

Charlie Brown: If I start writ – ing

now when I'm not real – ly rest – ed it could up – set

my think – ing which is not good at all, I'll get a fresh

start to – mor – row, and it's not due 'til Wednes–day, so I'll

have all of Tues – day, un – less some – thing should hap – pen.

Why does this al – ways hap – pen, I should be out – side

play – ing, get – ting fresh air and sun – shine. I work best

un – der pres – sure, and there'll be lots of pres – sure if

I wait 'til to – mor – row, I should start writ – ing now;

But if I start writ – ing now when I'm not real – ly

rest – ed, it could up – set my think – ing, which is no

good at all.

Lucy: The name of the rab – bit was Pe – ter. Twen-ty–

four, twen-ty-five, twen-ty-six, twen-ty-sev'n, twen-ty-eight, twen – ty – nine,

thir – ty! Ha!

Schroeder: Down came the staff on his head. Smash!

And Rob – in fell like a sack full of lead. Crash! The Sher – iff

laughed, and he left him for dead. Ah! But he was wrong.

Lucy: Thir – ty-five, thir – ty – six, thir – ty –

sev'n, thir – ty – eight, thir – ty – nine, for – ty.

Schroeder: Just then

an ar – row flew in, Whing! It was a sign for the fight to

be – gin, Zing! And then it looked like the Sher – iff would

win. Ah! But not for long.

A – way they ran. Just like rab-bits

who run a lot. As you can tell from the sto –

ry, of Pe – ter Rab – bit, which this re – port,

is a – bout.

Charlie Brown: How do they ex–pect us to write a

Lucy: There were veg – 'ta – bles in the gar – den
Book Re–port, of an – y qual – i – ty in

such as car – rots and spin – ach and on – ions and
just two days? How

let – tuce and turn – ips and pars – ley and o – kra and cab – bage and
can they conspire to make life so mis – 'ra – ble

string beans and par–snips, to – ma – toes, po – ta – toes, as – par – a – gus, cau–
and so ef – fec – tive – ly in so

li – flow – er, rhu – barb and chives
man – y ways.

Linus: Not to mention the extreme pressure exerted on him by his...

. . . deeply rooted rivalry with Flopsy and Mopsy and Cottontail

Lucy: Pe – ter

Charlie Brown: If I

Schroeder: The

Rab – bit is this stu – pid book a – bout this stu – pid rab –
start writ – ing now when I'm not real – ly rest –
name of this book a – bout which

---

bit who steals veg – 'ta – bles from oth – er peo – ple's gar
ed, It could up – set my think – ing, which is
this book re – port is a – bout

– dens, Gar – dens, Gar – dens. Sev – en – ty –
not good at all. Not good at all.
is, Pe – ter Rab – bit, Pe – ter Rab – bit.

---

five, sev – en – ty – six, sev – en – ty – sev'n, sev – en – ty – eight,
Oh ——————
All for one, ev – 'ry man does his part.

sev – en – ty – nine,   eigh – ty,   eigh – ty – one,

First   thing   af   –   ter

Oh————————————————————————

eigh – ty – two,   And   they were. ver – y,   ver – y,   ver – y,   ver – y,

din – ner   I'll   start.

ver – y   ver – y   hap – py   to   be home.   Nine–ty–

Schroeder: The   end.

four, nine – ty–five,   The   ver – y, ver–y,   ver   –   y   end.————————

Charlie Brown: A   Book

Re – port   on   Pe – ter   Rab – bit.

Linus: A   –   men.

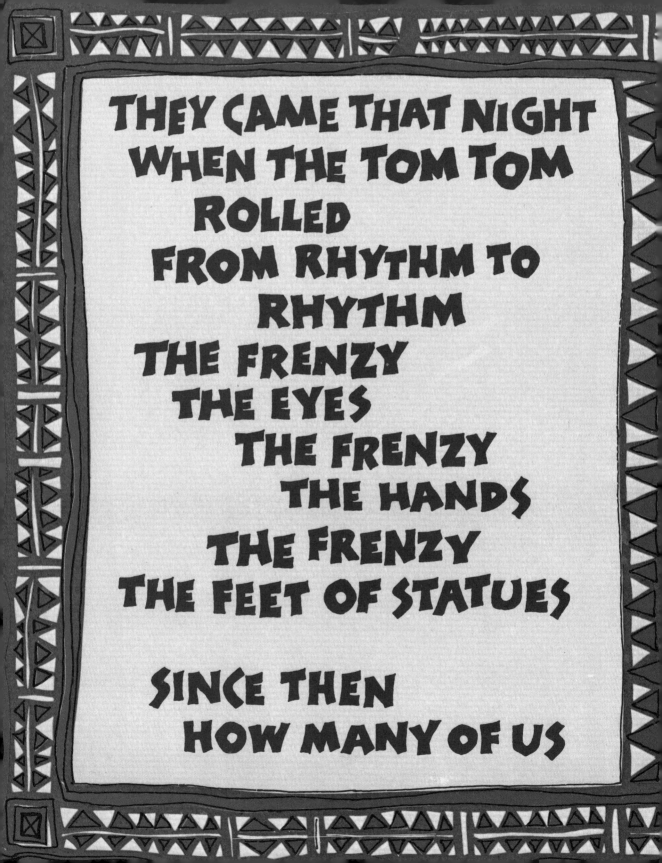

THEY CAME THAT NIGHT
WHEN THE TOM TOM
ROLLED
FROM RHYTHM TO
RHYTHM
THE FRENZY
THE EYES
THE FRENZY
THE HANDS
THE FRENZY
THE FEET OF STATUES

SINCE THEN
HOW MANY OF US

ARE DEAD
SINCE THEY CAME
THAT NIGHT
WHEN THE TOM TOM
ROLLED
FROM RHYTHM TO
RHYTHM
THE FRENZY
THE EYES
THE FRENZY
THE HANDS
THE FRENZY
THE FEET OF STATUES

BY LEON DAMAS   DESIGN/LETTERING BY LYNDA & RAY BARBER

The Lion in Love.

It happened in the days of old that a Lion fell in love with a Woodman's daughter and asked for her hand in marriage. The Woodman was not much pleased with the offer and declined the honor of so dangerous an alliance. But upon the Lion threatening him with his royal displeasure the poor man decided to change his mind. "I feel greatly flattered," he said "with your proposal; but, noble sir, what great teeth you have got! And what great claws you have got! Where is the damsel that would not be frightened at such weapons as these? You must have your teeth plucked out and your claws cut off before you can be a suitable bridegroom for my daughter." The Lion straightway submitted, for he was too much in love to hesitate. Now the Woodman was no longer afraid of the tamed and disarmed bully, and he seized a stout cudgel and drove the unreasonable suitor from his door.

The Horse and the Lion.

A Lion, seeing a fine plump Nag, had a great mind to eat a bit of him, but knew not how to get him into his power. At last he bethought to make himself out as a physician, who having gained experience by his travels into foreign countries had made himself capable of curing any kind of malady incident to any kind of beast. He hoped by this means to get an easier admittance among the cattle and find an opportunity to carry out his design. The Horse, who saw through his plan, was resolved to be even with him. So, humoring the thing as if he suspected nothing, he prayed the Lion to give him his advice about a thorn he had got in his foot. The Lion readily agreed and asked to see the foot, upon which the Horse lifted up one of his legs and while the Lion pretended to be poring earnestly over his foot, gave him such a kick in the face as quite stunned him, and left him sprawling upon the ground.

It is sometimes permissible to repel craft by cunning.

PENCIL DRAWING
BY JENNIFER PERROTT

The moon is RUN behind the tree.
GABRIELLA,
RUN.

Poem and Illustrations by Ronald Himler

Gabriella, you've RUN, LEAVE YOUR PLAY. stayed too long.
RUN, RUN AWAY.

FISH SWIM IN THE SKY, GABRIELLA.

THE NIGHT HAS TURNED UPSIDE DOWN.

RUN, GABRIELLA, RUN, RUN.

RUN TO THE HOUSE ON THE HILL.

DON ANTONIO RIDING NEAR HEARS GABRIELLA'S CRY.

THE HOOVES OF HIS PONY FLASH STEEL.

DON ANTONIO, KNIGHT WITHOUT FEAR.

HE STRIKES WITH HIS LANCE AND SHIELD.

A THOUSAND LIGHTS SHATTER THE WATER

114

GABRIELLA, THE FISH ARE RETURNING.

GABRIELLA, THERE IS NOTHING TO FEAR.

NOW TWO MAKE THEIR WAY TOGETHER TO THE BRIGHT HOUSE ON THE HILL.

Funny the Way Different Cars Start

A POEM BY DOROTHY W. BARUCH

Funny the way
Different cars start.
Some with a chunk and a jerk,
Some with a cough and puff of smoke
Out of the back,
Some with only a little click—with hardly any noise.

Funny the way
Different cars run.
Some rattle and bang,
Some whirrr,
Some knock and knock.
Some purr
And hummmmm
Smoothly on with hardly any noise.

118

Schenectady

A POEM BY EVE MERRIAM

Although I've been to Kankakee
And Kalamazoo and Kokomo,
The place I've always wanted to go,
The city I've always wanted to see
Is Schenectady.

Schenectady, Schenectady,
Though it's hard to pronounce correctly,
I plan to go there directly.

Schenectady, Schenectady,
Yes, I want to connect with Schenectady,
The town I select is Schenectady,
I elect to go to Schenectady,
I'll take any trek to Schenectady,
Even wash my neck for Schenectady,
So expect me next at Schenectady,
Check and double check
Schenectady!

A STORY BY ALEXANDER RESNIKOFF,
ILLUSTRATIONS BY PETER LIPPMAN

Ming and Ling

Once on a time
In the land of Ming,
there was a king
whose name was Ming —
because he was the king
Of Ming.

Now, Ming had everything . . .

A beautiful castle, a golden building
(the walls were covered with golden gilding),
gardens blooming in the spring,
in each garden a golden swing,
golden fish in silver spring,
golden bees that didn't sting,
silver bells on a silver string,
and on each hand five fingers —
and on each finger, a golden ring.

Next to the land of Ming
was the land of Ling,
and in the land of Ling
there was a king
whose name, of course, was Ling
because he was the king
Of Ling.

Ling also had everything . . .

He too had a castle, a golden building
(the walls were covered with golden gilding).
He too had gardens in the spring,
and in each garden a golden swing,
and golden fish in a silver spring,
and golden bees that didn't sting,
and silver bells on a silver string,
And on each hand he too had five fingers —
And on each finger a golden ring.

Now Ming and Ling were friends.
Each evening they went visiting,
singing,
strolling,
walking
talking
reasoning
questioning
whispering
wondering . . .

The friendship of Ming and Ling
was a beautiful thing.
One day in the spring
Ming, the king of Ming,
was wandering
Between the lands of Ming and Ling
And lost a ring —
the smallest ring from his smallest finger —
Just a little gold ring —
It didn't worry Ming.

121

Later in the spring
King Ling found the ring
atwinkling in the grass.
And so he picked it up.
It didn't mean a thing to King Ling.
He had everything.

But next evening when Ming and Ling
were visiting,
Ming saw the ring, and — what a terrible thing! —
without considering,
his eyes glittering,
He yelled at the King of Ling:
"That's my ring!"

"This is not your ring!"
cried the King of Ling,
and so they started quarreling
and dickering
and bickering
and clamoring
and glowering
and blistering
and simmering
and menacing
and bullying
and as one thing leads to another,
soon Ming and Ling
were brandishing their swords.

Ming swang at Ling!
And back at Ming came a swing —
a dueling,
a harrying, a parrying,
thrusting, busting,
sneering, jeering,
fearing, yet persevering,
king against king!
Such fools, Ming and Ling! —

And then — the strangest thing —
as they were dueling
all the bells in the land of Ling
and all the bells in the land of Ming
began to ring!
Ding! Dong! Ding! Dong! Ding!

"Hurry," someone said. "Save the king!"
And all the knights to king adhering
jumped upon their horses rearing
whipping, spurring, walloping,
They rode out agalloping!
Ding! Dong! Ding! Dong! Ding!
"Hurry, save the king!"

And so the army of Ming
met the army of Ling.
And through the night the might inciting
Each knight began a knight deknighting.
The flashes of their swords alighting
As lightning in the night igniting,
Each blow another blow inviting
and in the fright'ning fight delighting
on they went smiting, biting, fighting,
teeth gnashing,
daggers slashing,
horses dashing,
weapons clashing,
lashing
thrashing
smashing . . .

And all for a little gold ring.
A terrible, terrible thing . . .

A̲nd in the morning,
                    mourning.

The castle of Ming,
. . . beautiful castle, a golden building,
The walls once covered with golden gilding . . .
                    crumbling.

The castle of Ling,
. . . those blooming gardens in the spring,
Those golden bees that didn't sting . . .
                    burning.

The knights so bravely fighting
. . . each blow a blow inviting
And in the fright'ning fight delighting . .
                    dying.

And the kings of Ming and Ling?
                    crying —

crying —
crying —
crying —

In the midst of all the dying
lying on the ground, crying,
trembling
rememb'ring
relenting
repenting
lamenting . . .

Wounded King of Ling,
bleeding, suffering,
through the tears he was shedding
saw a shadow spreading
growing, nearing, stretching, reaching —
he turned to it, his eyes beseeching.
Was it death on wing
coming for King Ling?

No, it was the hand of Ming,
no more threatening,
no longer wrath and death purporting,
no longer smashing, clawing, thwarting,
but rather back to life exhorting
in silent offering.

The hand of Ming
touched the hand of Ling
and all evil superseding,
Ming gently bound the wounds still bleeding
and lifting, heaving, praying, pleading,
carefully started leading
his friend away from fires spreading.

The king of Ming
now truly was a king.

And later in the spring —
Oh, what a wond'rous thing!

The golden sun as she was rising
saw a supersight surprising,
saw a supersight appealing,
for there, under common ceiling
Were Ming and Ling, their wounds now healing,
impoverished, but rich in feeling,
toiling,
    working,
        building,
           singing.
Again the silver bells were ringing,
oh yes! the silver bells were jingling,

Merrily now, no war akindling,
For Ming and Ling again were mingling . . .

in a new beginning . . . . .

Staying Alive

A SURVIVAL POEM BY DAVID WAGGONER

Staying alive in the woods is a matter of calming down
At first and deciding whether to wait for rescue,
Trusting to others,
Or simply to start walking and walking in one direction
Till you come out — or something happens to stop you.
By far the safer choice
Is to settle down where you are, and try to make a living
Off the land, camping near water, away from shadows.

It may be best to learn what you have to learn without a gun.
Not killing but watching birds and animals go
In and out of shelter
At will. Following their example, build for a whole season:
Facing across the wind in your lean-to,
You may feel wilder,
But nothing, not even you, will have to stay in hiding.

Eat no white berries;
Spit out all bitterness. Shooting at anything
Means hiking further and further every day
To hunt survivors;
        If you hurt yourself,
stumbling, wading, and climbing,
                        no one will comfort you
Or take your temperature.

If you have no matches, a stick and a fire-bow
Will keep you warmer,
Or the crystal of your watch, filled with water, held up to the sun
Will do the same in time. In case of snow
Drifting toward winter.
Don't try to stay awake through the night, afraid of freezing —
The bottom of your mind knows all about zero;
It will turn you over
And shake you till you waken. If you have trouble sleeping
Even in the best of weather, jumping to follow
With eyes strained to their corners
The unidentifiable noises of the night and feeling
Bears and packs of wolves nuzzling your elbow.
Remember the trappers
Who treated them indifferently and were left alone.

But if you decide, at last, you must break through
In spite of all danger,
Think of yourself by time and not by distance, counting
Wherever you're going by how long it takes you;
No other measure
Will bring you safe to nightfall.

                     Follow no streams: they run
Under the ground or fall into wilder country.

When your mind runs into circles, remember the stars
                                        And the moss.

                                                If it should rain
Or the fog should roll the horizon in around you,
Hold still for hours
Or days if you must, or weeks, for seeing is believing
In the wilderness.

        And if you find a pathway,
Wheel-rut, or fence-wire,
Retrace it left or right; someone knew where he was going
Once upon a time, and you can follow
Hopefully, somewhere,
Just in case.

        There may even come, on some uncanny evening,
A time when you're warm and dry, well fed, not thirsty,
Uninjured, without fear,
When nothing, either good or bad, is happening.
This is called staying alive. It's temporary.
What occurs after
Is doubtful. You must always be ready
for something to come bursting
Through the far edge of a clearing, running toward you,
Grinning from ear to ear

And hoarse with welcome. Or something crossing and hovering
Overhead, as light as air, like a break in the sky.
Wondering what you are.
Here you are face to face with the problem
of recognition.

Having no time to make smoke, too much to say,
You should have a mirror
With a tiny hole in the back for better aiming, for reflecting
Whatever disaster you can think of, to show
The way you suffer.
These body signals have universal meaning:
If you are lying
Flat on your back with arms outstretched behind you,
You say you require
Emergency treatment; if you are standing erect and holding
Arms horizontal, you mean you are not ready;
If you hold them over
Your head, you want to be picked up. Three of anything
Is a sign of distress.

Afterward, if you see
No ropes, no ladders,
No maps or messages falling, no searchlights or trails blazing,
Then, chances are, you should be prepared to burrow
Deep for a deep winter.

BIRDS

A POEM BY RAY FABRIZIO

A bird flies and has wings
And it certainly sings

A bird when it sings is always certain.
It sings and sings about certain things,
Like flying and having wings
Or being only a bird in a tree
And free

Free is when you are being certain
And wanting to sing certainly
About certain things.

A bird is free and certainly sings.
It sings and sings about flying
      and having wings
Or being always a certain thing
When it is only a bird in a tree
Singing certainly
And free.

ILLUSTRATION BY ETIENNE DELESSERT, THROUGH THE COURTESY OF GAC PROPERTIES, INC.

The Flow of the River

A few winters ago, clothed heavily against the weather, I wandered several miles along one of the tributaries of that same Platte (river) I had floated down years before. The land was stark and ice-locked. The rivulets were frozen, and over the marshlands the willow thickets made such an array of vertical lines against the snow that tramping through them produced strange optical illusions and dizziness. On the edge of a frozen backwater, I stopped and rubbed my eyes. At my feet a raw prairie wind had swept the ice clean of snow. A peculiar green object caught my eye; there was no mistaking it.

Staring up at me with all his barbels spread pathetically, frozen solidly in the wind-ruffled ice, was a huge familiar face. It was one of those catfish of the twisting channels, those dwellers in the yellow murk, who had been about me and beneath me on the day of my great voyage. Whatever sunny dream had kept him paddling there while the mercury plummeted downward and that Cheshire smile froze slowly, it

AN EXCERPT FROM THE BOOK
THE IMMENSE JOURNEY BY LOREN EISELEY,
PICTURE BY ED YOUNG

would be hard to say. Or perhaps he was trapped in a blocked channel and had simply kept swimming until the ice contracted around him. At any rate, there he would lie till the spring thaw.

At that moment I started to turn away, but something in the bleak, whiskered face reproached me, or perhaps it was the river calling to her children. I termed it science, however— a convenient rational phrase I reserve for such occasions—and decided that I would cut the fish out of the ice and take him home. I had no intention of eating him. I was merely struck by a sudden impulse to test the survival qualities of high-plains fishes, particularly fishes of this type who get themselves immured in oxygenless ponds or in cut-offs oxbows buried in winter drifts. I blocked him out as gently as possible and dropped him, ice and all, into a collecting can in the car. Then we set out for home.

Unfortunately, the first stages of what was to prove a remarkable resurrection escaped me. Cold and tired after a long drive, I deposited the can with its melting water and ice in the basement. The accompanying corpse I anticipated I would either dispose of or dissect on the following day. A hurried glance had revealed no signs of life.

To my astonishment, however, upon descending into the basement several hours later, I heard stirrings in the receptacle and peered in. The ice had melted. A vast pouting mouth ringed with sensitive feelers confronted me, and the creature's gills labored slowly. A thin stream of silver bubbles rose to the surface and popped. A fishy eye gazed up at me protestingly.

"A tank," it said. This was no Walden pickerel. This was a yellow-green, mud-grubbing, evil-tempered inhabitant of floods and droughts and cyclones. It was the selective product of the high continent and the waters that pour across it. It had outlasted prairie blizzards that left cattle standing frozen upright in the drifts.

"I'll get the tank," I said respectfully.

He lived with me all that winter, and his departure was totally in keeping with his sturdy, independent character. In the spring a migratory impluse or perhaps sheer bordom struck him. Maybe, in some little lost corner of his brain, he felt, far off, the pouring of the mountain waters through the sandy coverts of the Platte. Anyhow, something called to him, and he went. One night when no one was about, he simply jumped out of his tank. I found him dead on the floor next morning. He had made his gamble like a man—or, I should say, a fish. In the proper place it would not have been a fool's gamble. Fishes in the drying shallow of intermittent praire streams who feel their confinement and have the impulse to leap while there is yet time may regain the main channel and survive. A million ancestral years had gone into that jump, I thought as I looked at him a million years of climbing through prairie sunflowers and twining in and out through the pillared legs of drinking mammoth.

COOL BEAUTIFUL · FINE·'N'·DANDY · ON·TIME · JOHNNY·ON·THE·SPOT · LICKETY·SPLIT · DELIGHTFUL · Pleasant · GOOD DEAL · SOMETHING ELSE · GREAT · TOO MUCH · VERY KEEN · PLEASANT · QUICK·AS·A·BUNNY · SPEEDY · WALLET · EASY·ON·THE·WALLET · FAST · SWIFT · MONEY · Neat · SAVING · YEAH·YEAH·YEAH · THRIFTY · FREQUENT · OUT OF SIGHT

COURTESY OF PACIFIC SOUTHWEST AIRLINES

South African Scope, a pamphlet, shows
me a picture of a female laughing dove who,
with her mate, built a nest on the wind-
screen wiper of an automobile in a
Durban showroom. I have seen
the bird and the nest. The staff
of the showroom guarded the
bird. The vehicle was not
sold until the eggs
hatched and the
fledglings flew.

I want you to know about the staff in Durban
and the flying laughing birds.

by Hollis Summers, picture by Sal Murdocca

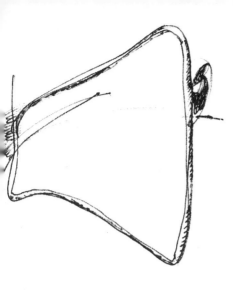

The Power of Eye

A story by Dawn C. Thomas, drawings by Bill Shields

Rudyard Riseup
was our school bus driver.
To say he wasn't well-liked
by the kids
is to put it mildly.
Behind his back they called him
Ridiculous Riseup.
To his face they would say,
Mr. Riseup.
For this tale,
I'll just call him Rudyard,
since I'm not fronting him
or backing him.
And all I'm going to do
is talk about him.

Well, Rudyard thought us kids
were the dumbest,
ugliest things around.
Why he drove a school bus
none of us could figure out.
He didn't like kids
and he wasn't a good driver.
That may surprise
some of you.
But you see,
we live in one of those
cities of tomorrow.
So our highways are trackways.
All you do is sit behind the wheel
and everything is done for you
automatically.

But, as I was saying,
Rudyard wasn't much good
at anything else
and they still hadn't found a way
of automating
finding lost things on a bus
or stopping fights,
so the town paid Rudyard
to see to that.

Now, Rudyard was
a mean man.
Above all,
he had a snitching personality.
Whatever he heard us kids
talking about on the bus
was sure to get back to our parents
via the human newspaper, Rudyard.
We developed
a kind of sign language.
That worked swell
for a while.
One morning,
I got on the bus
and almost fell right off again.
Rudyard had a big panoramic mirror
installed in front of the bus.
He now could see
the finger action.
Then he got annoyed
because he couldn't
understand finger talk.
The next thing I knew
he told my parents they ought
to have my kidneys checked
since I always sat on the bus
with my hand up
like I had to go to the bathroom.

I mean,
things like that
are embarrassing.
Then too, Rudyard
was not a conversationalist.
You could never
get him to answer.
He had thick eyebrows
that hung down over his eyelids.
Instead of answering you
he'd raise an eyebrow.
Boy! That was a weird sight.
His eyebrows resembled
the tip of a paint brush
looking for an easel.
He'd make us miss our stops
and if you had music class
you'd be sure to walk home.
Rudyard would just pass any kid
who was carrying an instrument.
I mean,
I really can't say
that I blamed him
after what happened
one afternoon in November.
You see, we have
this real educated boy
in our school.
And of all things
he plays the French horn.
Well now,
every November
our school gives this concert.

And any child
who can make a toot,
no matter how flat,
is in the concert.
But Hesper,
he was good at playing
the French horn,
so he was going to solo.
Now us guys had planned
a terrific surprise for him.
The afternoon of the concert,
just as rehearsal was over,
we stuffed a few rotten eggs
into that horn.
Imagine our surprise
when Hesper got on the bus
dragging that horn case.
So, he sits down
on the long back seat
and pulls out his horn.
I guess he wanted
to run through
his evening's selections.
Well, knowing
that some drastic action
was about to be put down,
I ducked.

Hesper blew gently at first
and nothing happened.
Then puffing up,
like a combination case
of mumps and swollen glands,
he blew with all his might.
Well sir, the first egg
goes zinging through the bus
and lands,
that's right, you guess it,
right on Rudyard's head.
When the shell cracked
and the smell ran through the bus,
kids were falling out of their seats
gasping for air.
I told you Rudyard was mean.
He locked the window control up front
and not a breath of fresh air
came into the bus
during the entire trip home.
Somehow I managed
to stagger into the house
only to have my mom announce
that we
were having egg salad for supper.

Well, I'm giving
all of this information about Rudyard
so you can
kind of get to know him
like I do.
But the facts I just told you
have nothing to do with my tale,
which is really Rudyard's tale,
depending on how you look at it.

Now there was this girl
in our school
who came from a long line
of witches.
We all knew it,
but it didn't bother us.
We never tried to pull
any of this
drastic action business on her.
Rudyard knew
about her ancestors,
but he didn't believe it.
Well,
one day he made the mistake
of passing Hermine,
for that was the girl's name,
at the school stop.
You see,
she had the instrument case
and two baseball bats
and some other junk.
Well, Rudyard slowed down,
took a look
and drove right on by.
We were booing and hissing
and generally
putting down drastic action
when suddenly the bus stopped.

Then it went into reverse
and we were back at the corner.
The door opened
and up jumped Hermine
and all her junk.
She stared at Rudyard,
then calmly sat down,
neatly tucking her trappings
under the seat.

Rudyard scratched his head.
We sat there speechless.
Naturally, we knew
what was happening.
Boy, that Hermine
certainly had
some powerful drastic action
and I was glad that I had never
put anything down on her.
Throughout the trip home,
Rudyard
sort of looked perplexed
and tried to decipher the finger talk
through his panoramic mirror.
And all the time
Hermine sat there
reading some book called
The Power of Eye.

Believe me, the kids were talking.
But we hadn't seen the last of it.
Hermine's stop was coming up.
So she gets up,
piling her stuff in her arms,
and moves
towards the front of the bus.
By now, all is hushed
and what wasn't naturally hushed
was shushed by kids
who wanted to hear
what was going to happen.

Rudyard pushes the control button
to make sure
that the bus
and the curb are even.
Just as Hermine
is stepping down,
she turns around,
smiles sweetly and says,
"Good luck,"
looking Rudyard dead in the eye.
Now, what she said was nothing
for any reply or conversation
and knowing Rudyard's eyebrow talk
we just figures
this was the end of it.
I almost jumped out of my seat
when suddenly
Rudyard's mouth opens
and I hear, "Quack, quack!"

Some of the kids were falling
out of their seats with laughter.
Hermine turns around again
and says,
"I said good luck,
not Donald Duck,"

I don't know how it got started,
but as each of us
left the bus that night
we'd holler out, "Good luck,"
and sure enough
Rudyard would answer,
"Quack, quack!"

143

The following day
I was up and ready for school
before the television clock came on.
My mother suspicioned
that something was in the wind,
but her automatic cleaning man
had lost a tube
and she had no time
to give me the third degree.
Now,
from yesterday's long experiences
I was more than careful
of letting anybody
concentrate on me too long
with their eyes.
I believed
that eyes were the source
of Hermine's drastic action power.

The school bus
seemed to take forever that day.
Suddenly it smoothly came
down the trackway.
Most of the kids
were jammed in seats
in the front.
Nobody wanted to miss
a speck of snuff
that might fly today.
The bus was real quiet-like.
There was no finger action.
We sat there,
riding and peeking out
to see if Hermine
was standing on her corner.
You know, by life, she was.

Well, we're riding along.
Hermine has been on the bus
for about five minutes.
Naturally
we're all more than disappointed
that nothing had happened.
Rudyard feels confident again.

He's passing kids,
working the controls
to keep fresh air out,
looking at us
through the panoramic mirror
and in general
displaying his personality.
Hermine
has stopped reading her book
and is staring at Rudyard
in disbelief.
I guess if I had been exposed
to her drastic action
the way Rudyard had been,
believe me, I wouldn't try
anything with anyone
with her anywhere around.
But Rudyard
was long on meanness
and short on smart.
Well, anyway,
I look up at the window
and I notice
that the bus is traveling
on a new trackway.
It wasn't a detour
on the way to school
and I couldn't honestly say
that this stretch
was at all familiar to me.
The other kids noticed too
and after awhile
we started talking about it.
Then it hit me.

Boy, did it ever hit me.
Rudyard was not behind
the wheel of the bus.
There was Hermine's mother,
broomstick and all,
pushing and pulling
those automatic controls.
I shivered, 'cause I knew
between mother and daughter
us kids
were in for some drastic action
like we had never seen before
and might never see again.
I started squirming around,
trying to find out
what had happened to Rudyard.
A fly,
complete with bus driver's cap
starts buzzing by my window,
trying to get out.

My eyes
must have rolled in my head
faster than Jack
came tumbling down that hill.
This was bad.
Indeed, it was.

The kids started shooing that fly
and swinging their sweaters
and jackets at it.
Then most of them discovered
that the fly
not only looked like Rudyard,
but was dressed like him.
Well, as much as they
disliked Rudyard,
nobody
hated him enough to kill him.
So they just kept brushing him
off their clothes and books
everytime he tried to light.

Well, this business
was the talk of the school
and that afternoon,
kids who didn't live in our area
piled on our bus,
pretending to be invited
to other children's homes,
just to witness the bus show.
But nothing happened
and by the next morning
Rudyard
was back to his old tricks again.

When I first started this tale,
I thought Rudyard was mean
or just disliked children.
But now,
in getting down
to the tail of this tale,
I do believe
Rudyard was just stupid.
Now the next morning,
Hermine is waiting on the corner
with more junk than ever
and a guitar case
and a violin case.
I forgot to tell you
she was really talented
and played
almost every instrument
in the orchestra.

Rudyard doesn't even slow down.
He pushed and pulled controls,
trying to keep
a steady course
and steady speed.
He went right by Hermine.
When he was
about two blocks away from her
the bus stops,
goes into reverse
and backs up
to get Hermine.
Now for the first time
Rudyard looks upset,
but he makes out
like he's running late.

We never did
get to school that day.
And I'm about
to tell you why.
The next time I looked up,
Hermine's mother
was perched on her broomstick
and that was perched on the seat
behind the driver's control panel.
We looked for the fly,
but he was nowhere in sight.
The bus starts to leave the track
and I won't tell you how,
for you'll never believe me.
Soon we're all standing in a field
in front of a large pot.
Man, that was the biggest pot
I had ever seen.

Little women, about a foot high
were swinging on the handle,
looking down into the pot, smiling.

"You see," said Hermine,
smiling sweetly,
"these are Rudyard's godmothers,
fairy godmothers, if you please.
They decided
to put him together
all over again,
just to see what ingredient
had been left out."

Some of the kids stood there shaking.
Others put their hands up
trying to cover their faces.
I edged up
closer to the pot to peek in.
Hermine just wasn't putting us on.

There were
about fifty jars
in that pot
with all different
labels on them.
One said soul,
another said heart,
another said intelligence,
and so on.
One godmother
was down in the pot
with what looked
like a big castor oil spoon
just a-scooping and a-dipping
a little from here
and a lot from there.
It took about the whole day
to dip and scoop,
boil and heat.
At last
Hermine motioned us
back on the bus.
Sure enough,
there was Rudyard
with a smile on his face,
sitting behind
the panel control.

"Good afternoon,"
he greeted us.
"You big boys
help the little ones up.
While you kids
were at school
I put in a special rack
to hold your instruments
so that none of them
would be broken
while going back and forth."
Old Rudyard
was all sweetness and light.
After awhile we got used to him.
Now he was so good
he almost killed us with kindness.
    Well now,
        this tale could go on.
        I could tell you
        how we missed the fun
        of trying to get
        Rudyard's goat.
        I could tell you
        how with him being so nice
    we didn't dare fight
    or say unkind things
    in front of him,
        behind him, or anywhere else.
    But I'm sure
    you can figure things out
for yourself.

The important thing is that we learned some very important things. First of all, be happy with what you've got, because you always know what that is but you don't know what you will be getting.

Above all, school bus drivers aren't meant to be loved, they're just there to do a job.

A Story in Cartoon

Growing Up, Growing Older

A POEM BY MARY MARTIN KREAMER

Born bare; loud wail; need care; much love.
Rest, wake, howl, feed, have bath, play, grow.
Find hand, find toes, seek face, know arms, love.
Walk, fall, weep, rise, walk, talk, play game, glow.
Hear lore, hear tale, hear song.

Skip rope, toss ball, garb doll, boss pets.
Slam door, dash here, rush fast, hear call, walk slow.
Take food, like junk, yell loud, fall down, jump, howl.
Love sire, some days. Bump toes, snap bone, need care.
Read book, tell tale, sing song.

Snow, sled; rain, wade; wind, kite; lake, swim; seas, sail.
Grow tall, grow wide, teen aged, glib, flip, keen.
Skip meal, gulp coke, love pals, also pets, need task.
Care much, hide same. Ache, long, seek, have idea, grow!
Read book, tell tale, sing song.

Seek what: Life? Love? Fame? Ease? Loot? Play? Wine?
Much fuss. Muse, moon, mood, mope. Idea? Grow wise. Gain wits.
Wise grad. Find post, good site, glad days. Earn keep; more.
Hold hand, kiss lips, love mate. Peal, bell, peal! Tied with ring.
Read book, tell tale, sing song.

Make home, Feud some, love more. Care. Vote, Ease ache, cure ills.
Baby with body, legs, toes, arms, chin, ears, hair, lips, eyes!
Joys many. Full life. Busy, busy. Work, play, love, care, busy.
Tire, rest, ease, loaf, vote, love, care! Work done, life over.
Book read, tale told, song sung.

To Satch

A POEM BY SAMUEL W. ALLEN

Sometimes I feel like I will never stop
Just go on forever
Til one fine mornin'
I'm gonna reach up and grab me a handfulla stars
Swing out my long lean leg
And whip three hot strikes burnin' down the heavens
And look over at God and say
How about that!

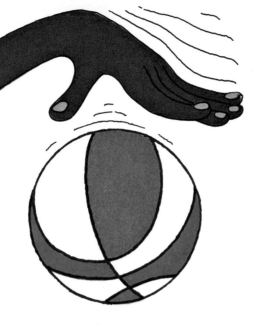

A POEM BY STEPHEN ANDREWS

Big Lew Dunks One Through

The gangling center
fakes five directions
at once; stops, spins, jumps
grabs the high pass and
crams the ball down through.

153

The Alphabet Boat

The boat needs an anchor to keep us at rest. The boat needs a bird to perch on the bow.

The boat needs a captain to put us to sea.

The boat needs a dinghy to follow in tow.

The boat needs an east wind

to fill up the sails.

The boat needs a fair sky

for the long journey ahead.

The boat needs a galley to store biscuits and rum.

H The boat needs a horn to call **H** through the fog.

I The boat needs an iron keel to ride out a storm.

The boat needs a **J** jib sail; hoist the halyards high!

The boat needs **J** a kettle

K to brew coffee for the watch.

L The boat needs a long glass for spotting a whale.

M The boat needs a mainsail for speed in the gathering breeze.

The boat needs a northern **N** light to wink in the night.

The boat needs oars:

"Drive her, mates, **O** drive her!"

The boat **P** needs planks, sturdy pine and white oak.

The boat needs a quiet harbor, far from the swells and spray.

The boat needs a rudder to steer through the seas.

The boat needs a song to sing under the stars.

The boat needs a transom to carry her name.

The boat is called umiak if you are an Eskimo.

The boat needs

varnish for her branches of spars.

The boat needs a wheel to hold against tumbling waves.

The boat needs an X when it is a xebec.

The boat needs a yellow moon to pillow your dream.

The boat needs a zephyr, west winds home,

gentle  at your back.

Stupid

A POEM BY R. D. LAING

How clever has one to be to be stupid?
The others told her she was stupid. So she made
herself stupid in order not to see how stupid
they were to think she was stupid,
because it was bad to think they were stupid.
She preferred to be stupid and good,
rather than bad and clever.

It is bad to be stupid: she needs to be clever
to be so good and stupid.
It is bad to be clever, because this shows
how stupid they were
to tell her how stupid she was.

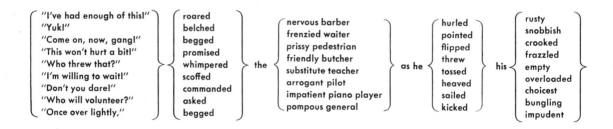

"I've had enough of this!"	roared		nervous barber		hurled		rusty
"Yuk!"	belched		frenzied waiter		pointed		snobbish
"Come on, now, gang!"	begged		prissy pedestrian		flipped		crooked
"This won't hurt a bit!"	promised		friendly butcher		threw		frazzled
"Who threw that?"	whimpered	the	substitute teacher	as he	tossed	his	empty
"I'm willing to wait!"	scoffed		arrogant pilot		heaved		overloaded
"Don't you dare!"	commanded		impatient piano player		sailed		choicest
"Who will volunteer?"	asked		pompous general		kicked		bungling
"Once over lightly,"	begged						impudent

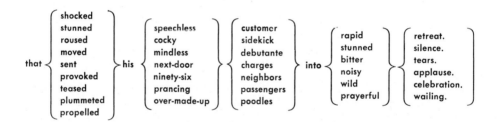

clippers	at the clock		came out with	wicked-looking	meat cleaver
nose	out the window		touched off	ten-round	Roman candle
finger	across the room		gave out with	flame-producing	string of oaths
street map	into the air		picked up	red hot	branding iron
tray	into the gutter	and	gobbled down	a foot-long	chain of wieners
brief case	out the door		broke out with	mind-blowing	buggy whip
sirloin steaks	over the counter		went into	dim-witted	rock concert
aids					egocentric explanation
student					
flight plans					

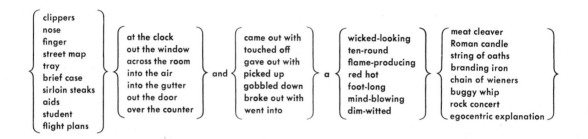

	shocked		speechless		customer		rapid	retreat.
	stunned		cocky		sidekick		stunned	silence.
	roused		mindless		debutante		bitter	tears.
	moved		next-door		charges		noisy	applause.
that	sent	his	ninety-six		neighbors	into	wild	celebration.
	provoked		prancing		passengers		prayerful	wailing.
	teased		over-made-up		poodles			
	plummeted							
	propelled							

Creative Writing Made Easy

ART AND POEM,
COURTESY OF THE PLAZA HOTEL, INC.

An old bamboo cutter, long, long ago
Saw a strange light in a bamboo grove
And found there a tiny fairy girl.
She lived as his daughter, and so lovely grew
That brave young men from all the land
Travelled there to ask her hand.

When autumn plucked the golden leaves
She became sad and often wept.
Her parents heard her mournful sobs
and came to her, asking why her tears.
She would not speak; would not explain
The reason for her grief and pain.

At last, one day, she told her tale
How, when the harvest moon was full,
She must return to a far-off place
Tho she loved her earthly home well.
The old ones were sad and tried to say
How much they loved her and wished her to stay.

The old man asked the brave young men
To help him guard the house that night.
So bright was the moon it seemed like day,
Then down a moonbeam the moonfolk came.
Not one man could move, nor utter a cry
And the young girl was taken up into the sky.

Karina feared the sea

alas
She also loved a whale.
The biggest strongest thing alive
From head to flippy tail.

She asked him each and every day
To make his life ashore.
She smiled and beckoned all she could,
But he would do more.

She sang him songs upon the rocks,
Of love and soul and grief,
The whale would listen gladly,
But he gave her no relief.

She asked the moon to stem the tide,
She begged the wind to blow
And send the whale upon the beach
That she his love might know.

The moon he tried to stem the tide,
The wind blew up a gale,
But the biggest strongest thing alive,
Refused to end this tale.

POEM AND PICTURE BY SAL MURDOCCA

161

Sea, Sand and Sorrow

What are heavy?
Sea, sand and sorrow.

What are brief?
Today and tomorrow.

What are frail?
Spring blossoms and youth.

What are deep?
The ocean and truth.

A POEM BY CHRISTINA G. ROSETTI
PAINTING BY AUDREY MENICUCCI

THE MAGIC FISHBONE —

adapted by Bill Martin, Jr.

an old story by Charles Dickens, pictures by Peter Lippman

Once upon a time there was a king and he had a queen.
She was the loveliest of her sex,
and he was the handsomest of his.
And they were always having children.
They had thirteen little daughters.
Princess Alicia, who was the eldest,
and the baby, who was the youngest, of course,
and spread out in-between
eleven other little princes and princesses.

Every day,
when good King Watkins the First went to his office,
he stopped first by the fish market to buy
a pound and a half of salmon,
"Not too near the tail!"
that being the queen's instructions—
(she was a very tidy housekeeper).

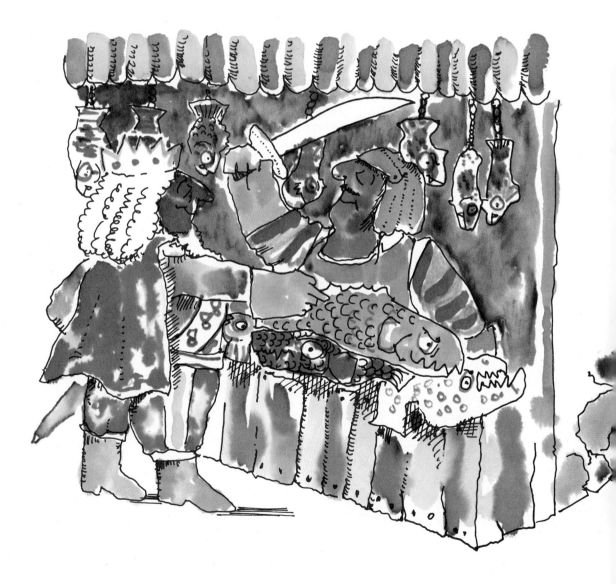

So with the pound and a half of salmon under his arm,
the king went off to his office
thinking how far off was pay day.
In fact, he was broke.
A cat followed him,
not because he was royalty
but because of the fish.

He turned around to shoo the cat away.
He found himself confronted by a little old lady
who was dressed in lavender and shot silk
and smelled dreadfully of toilet water
as women usually do.
She said,
"Good King Watkins the First, I believe."
Right off he knew she was the Grand Marina,
else how could she have known who he was?
And she said,
"You have a pound and a half of salmon under your arm!"

And he was sure, then,
         that she was the grandest fairy of all.
     She said, "When you get home tonight
         will you invite the Princess Alicia
       to partake of the salmon
         along with you and the queen,
         and when she is finished she will find upon the plate . . ."
       "Then what?" said the King.
     "Oh, hoity, toity," said the lady,
       "you're just like all adults, you're too impatient. . . .
     She will find upon the plate a little fish bone.
       Tell her to rub and shine it
     until it gleams like the mother-of-pearl
     and then it will make her wish come true—
providing, of course, that she wishes the right thing
—at the right time."

So the good king went off to the office that day
and thought all day about the magic fish bone.
He couldn't keep his mind on his work.

And when he got home that night
he invited the Princess Alicia to partake of the salmon,
and when she had finished eating,
surely enough, there on her plate
was a magic fish bone.
Then he told her the admonitions of the little old lady
and the little princess rubbed the fish bone
until it gleamed like the mother-of-pearl
and then she put it in her apron pocket
to make the wish at the right time.

Well, the next morning the good queen got out of bed
and she was a little sick in her stomach
and she fell fainting upon the floor.
Now Princess Alicia

       ran

          down-

            stairs

             and she got cold towels
and she brought up the big bottle of terrible-tasting medicine
that they were always giving the children
and she gave her mother a double tablespoonful.

When the good King Watkins came home from the office that night he said,

"My wife is in bed?"

"Yes."

"But Alicia!"

"Yes, Papa."

"Alicia, have you forgotten the fishbone?"

"No, Papa."

"Oh,"

said the King.

174

The next day when he came home
he found that the baby had fallen into the fire grate that day
and before they could fish him out
his face was banged and bruised.
He had cried all day.

And Princess Alicia, besides taking care of her mother,
had taken care of the baby,
and the eleven other little princes and princesses,
who were quite a trouble since she didn't have any help.
The butler and the maid had eloped just the week before.

WISH YOU WERE HERE

WISH YOU WERE HERE

WISH YOU WERE HERE

177

"Alicia!" said the King,
"Yes, Papa."
"Alicia, have you forgotten the fish bone?"
"No, Papa."
"Oh."
  The King sat down at the kitchen table
  and held his fat face in his hands.
"Papa, what's the matter?" the princess asked.
"Child, we have no money."
"None?"
"None."
"Papa, why don't you raise your salary?"
"Child, I tried to,
  but every bill I write is so fully written I have to veto it."
"Well, Father," said the Princess,
"when we've tried our best, and still can't succeed,
  I think that's the time to ask the help of others."
  So she reached into her pocket
  and she took out the magic fish bone
  and she made a wish upon it
  that it would immediately be pay day.

AND THEN THERE CAME DOWN THE CHIMNEY,

gold coins in such profusion
that they would have buried the baby
if they had not picked the little fellow up in a hurry.

Everyone said "HIP HIP HOORAY!"

But, of course, the King said it the loudest.

And then the window flew open . . .

and in came the Grand Marina riding in a golden coach drawn by six peacocks.

She stepped out of her coach and she opened her bejewelled fan and she said, "Good King Watkins, we meet again!"

With one wave of her bejewelled fan
the Queen became well
and she came down the stairs as fresh and healthy
as the day when she had been first married,
and she had on a gown of green velvet all brand new.

With another wave of the fan
all the children stopped being run-down-at-the-heels
and they were dressed in beautiful pink bloom velvet
with little blue caps with long feathers.
And she waved her fan once more
and the Princess Alicia was dressed for her wedding.
The only problem was—
there was no bridegroom.

She said,
"We'll take care of that, Alicia.
Good King Watkins, if you and your wife and the children
will be at the church in thirty minutes
you may attend the wedding of your daughter."
So
she helped the Princess Alicia into the coach
and she flew out the window into the dreadful London fog
until they found a likely-looking fellow
Prince Certain Personio.

His face was covered with barley sugar

and the good Grand Marina knew better

than to ask the boy to wash his face

so she took care of it with one wave of her fan

and took him off to the church.

It was a beautiful wedding,
and from what I understand
it was a shame that we were not all there
because there was plenty to eat and more to drink!

And after the wedding was over
they came out to the steps,
and the Grand Marina said,
"And now Good King Watkins, henceforth,
there will not be twelve, but thirteen pay days every year."

Everyone said, "HIP HIP HOORAY,"

but, of course,

the King said it

the loudest.

Turning to the bride and groom,
she said, "And now Alicia,
I will bless with fourteen children—

190

seven girls and—eight boys.
They will all be born with curly hair,
and they will all have had the chicken pox,
and that's as good as I can do for you."
(I guess you noticed that even the Grand Marina
has a little trouble with arithmetic.)

There was only one thing left,
and that was to take care of the magic fish bone.
It was done with one wave of the bejewelled fan
and the magic fish bone flew out of the princess' pocket
across the street
and down the throat
of that ugly little pug dog that is always barking
at six o'clock in the morning
disturbing the neighbors—
and he nearly choked—

and that was good.

195

Ties

A POEM BY DABNEY STUART

When I faded back to pass
Late in the game, as one
Who has been away some time
Fades back into memory,
My father, who had been nodding
At home by the radio,
Would wake, asking
My mother, who had not
Been listening, "What's the score?"
And she would answer, "Tied,"
While the pass I threw
Hung high in the brilliant air
Beneath the dark, like a star.

My Papa's Waltz

A POEM BY THEODORE ROETHKE

The whiskey on your breath
Could make a small boy dizzy;
But I hung on like death:
Such waltzing was not easy.

We romped until the pans
Slid from the kitchen shelf;
My mother's countenance
Could not unfrown itself.

The hand that held my wrist
Was battered on one knuckle;
At every step you missed
My right ear scraped a buckle.

You beat time on my head
With a palm caked hard by dirt,
Then waltzed me off to bed
Still clinging to your shirt.

My Favorite Teacher

In the following letter, a pupil describes the teacher who helped her most:

My English teacher, Mrs. C., has helped me more than any teacher I have ever had. You see, I am an Apache Indian girl and all my people speak Apache. Mrs. C. is teaching me to make my thoughts in English. This is not easy, because most of the time I think in Apache.

She helps me most too, because she understands me. Any time she sees me she says "hello" and I say "hello" to her. Then both of us will smile. When Mrs. C. smiles she has happy brown eyes, and I think of her as my mother. You see, I have no mother. She went away with a soft green wind a long time ago.

Last year I ran away from school. We have to be punished for that. Mrs. C. was very sad about it. She said that I must tell her exactly why I did it. When I told her how the "run-away" thought had hit my brain and made such a loud noise it just bounced me right down the road she laughed and said her thoughts bounced her around at times too. But she punished me just the same, because she had to be fair.

When I have thoughts running around inside me, I write them for her. When they are nice and beautiful we make poems out of them. We did this with the thoughts I wrote about our superintendent when he died. We named the poem "In Memoriam" and it was published by the "Arizona Highways" magazine. It will be in The Path to the Blue Skies, a book of creative writing by Indian children. Mrs. C. is having it published. I am sending a copy of this poem to you, because it is my best poem. I didn't know I could write poems until Mrs. C. came.

Our English room is the prettiest room we have. When we go in there we know we must work. Mrs. C. thinks we should learn to work and think like all American children. She knows we are Apache Indians, but she wants us to understand we are American citizens too.

Can't you see how Mrs. C. is helping me?

Sincerely,
Lucille Victor

In Memoriam

A POEM BY LUCILLE VICTOR, AGE 13
SAN CARLOS, ARIZONA INDIAN SCHOOL
PAINTING BY SAMUEL MAITIN

He is gone, friend of the Apache.
He sailed away on the deep blue waters of the wide, wide river.
The low notes of the soft green wind called him.
The song singing of the deep blue waters put him to sleep.
I saw him, this friend of the Apache,
      across the big, wide desk.
He said to me, "Do you like school, little Apache girl?"
My tongue stuck and would not say "Yes."
He smiled at me, and I heard him go home
      with the leaves sounding as he walked.
Now he is gone, friend of my people.
He sailed away with a soft green wind
      on the deep blue waters of the wide, wide river.

First Lesson

A POEM BY PHILIP BOOTH

Lie back, daughter, let your head
be tipped back in the cup of my hand.
Gently, and I will hold you. Spread
your arms wide, lie out on the stream
and look high at the gulls. A dead-
man's float is face down. You will dive
and swim soon enough
     where this tidewater
ebbs to the sea. Daughter, believe
me, when you tire on the long thrash
to your island, lie up, and survive.
As you float now, where I held you
and let you go, remember when fear
cramps your heart what I told you:
lie gently and wide to the light-year
stars, lie back,
     and the sea will hold you.

The Rebəl

A POEM BY MARI E. EVANS

When I
die
I'm sure
I will have a
Big Funeral . . .
Curiosity
seekers . . .
coming to see
if I
am really
Dead . . .
or just
trying to make
Trouble. . . .

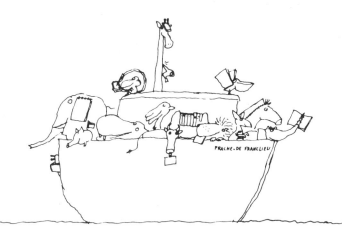

PRACHE·DE·FRANCLIEU

desclozeaux

Keep In Line

A POEM BY STEPHEN ANDREWS

Keep in line.
Keep in line.
Keep in line.
Keep in line.
Keep in line.
Keep in line.
Keep in line.
Keep in line.
Keep in line.
Keep in line.
Keep in line.
Keep in line.
 Don't get out of line.
Keep in line.
Keep in line.

While I Slept

A POEM BY ROBERT FRANCIS

While I slept, while I slept and the night grew colder
She would come to my bedroom stepping softly
And draw a blanket about my shoulder
While I slept.

While I slept, while I slept in the dark still heat
She would come to my bedside stepping coolly
And smooth the twisted troubled sheet
While I slept.

Now she sleeps, sleeps under quiet rain
While nights grow warm or nights grow colder
And I wake and sleep and wake again
While she sleeps.

CHRISTMAS EVE IN MEXICO

A SONG BY BILL MARTIN JR. AND AL CAIOLA,
HANDLETTERING BY RAY BARBER,
PAINTINGS BY VIC HERMAN

Once upon a hilltop
in Mexico
one Christmas eve
long long ago
I heard a shepherd boy
play his lone guitar

Once upon a hilltop
in Mexico
one Christmas eve
long long ago
I joined the shepherd boy
and his lone guitar

"WEDDING IN TEHUANTEPEC"

O what a carolling of Christmas eve
in Mexico
O what a heralding of Christmas eve
in Mexico
Our song made the mountains ring
that Christmas eve in Mexico
Our love made the angels sing
that Christmas eve in Mexico

Gentle shepherd from afar
how I wonder who you are
following that wondrous star
of Christmas eve in Mexico
with your lone guitar

Now upon a hilltop
in Mexico
each Christmas eve
since long ago
I seek the shepherd boy
and his lone guitar

Now upon the hilltop
in Mexico
each Christmas eve
since long ago
I miss the shepherd boy
and his lone guitar

O what a carolling that Christmas eve
long long ago
O what a heralding that Christmas eve
long long ago
O how the mountains ring
in memory of long ago
O how the angels sing
in reverie of long ago

Gentle shepherd from afar
lead me lead me where you are
come reflame that wonderous star
of Christmas eve in Mexico
with your lone guitar

BLUE-BUTTER-

It is a blue-butterfly

And with these sky-flakes

There is more unmixed

Than flowers will show

But these are flowers that

And now from having

They lie close over in the

Where wheels have freshly

FLY DAY

day here in the spring
down in flurry on flurry
color on the wing
for days unless they hurry.

fly and all but sing:
ridden out desire
wind and cling
sliced the April mire.

A POEM BY ROBERT FROST, HANDLETTERED AND DESIGNED BY RAY BARBER

A TALE BY MARK TWAIN,
ART AND LETTERING BY RAY BARBER

THE GOLDEN ARM

Once 'pon a time
dey wuz a monsus mean man,
en he live 'way out in de prairie
all 'lone by hisself, 'cept'n he had a wife.
En bimeby she died,
en he tuck en toted her way out dah in de prairie
en buried her. Well, she had a golden arm —
all solid gold, fum de shoulder down.
He wuz pow'ful mean — pow'ful;
en dat night he couldn't sleep,
caze he want dat golden arm so bad.

When it come midnight
he couldn't stan' it no mo';
so he git up,
he did, en tuck his lantern
en shoved out thoo de storm
en dug her up en got de golden arm;
en he bent his head down 'gin de win',
en plowed en plowed en plowed thoo de snow.
Den all on a sudden he stop

. . . en say: "My *lan'*, what's dat!"
En he listen
— en listen
— en de win' say "Bzzz-z-zzz"
— en den, way back yonder whah de grave is,
he hear a *voice!* —
he hear a voice all mix' up in de win'
— cain't hardly tell 'em 'part
—"Bzz-zzz
— W-h-o — g-o-t — m-y — g-o-l-d-e-n — *arm?*
— zzz-zzz
— W-h-o — g-o-t — m-y — g-o-l-d-e-n — *arm?*"

En he begin to shiver en shake,
en say, "Oh, my! *Oh*, my lan'!"
en de win' blow de lantern out,
en de snow en sleet blow in his face
en mos' choke him,
en he start a-plowin' knee-deep towards home
mos' dead, he so sk'yerd
— en pooty soon he hear de voice agin, en
. . . it 'us comin' *after* him!

"Bzzz — zzz — zzz
— W-h-o — g-o-t — m-y — g-o-l-d-e-n — *arm?*"

When he git to de pasture he hear it agin
— closter now, en a-*comin'*!
a-com-in' back dah in de dark en de storm

—"W-h-o — g-o-t — m-y — g-o-l-d-e-n — arm?!"

When he git to de house
he rush upstairs en jump in de bed
en kiver up, head and years,
en lay dah shiverin' en shakin'

— en den way out dah he hear it *agin!*

— en a-*comin'!* En bimeby he hear

— pat-pat-*hit's a-comin' up-stairs!*

Den he hear de latch open, en he *know* it's in de room!

Den pooty soon he know
it's a-*stannin' by de bed!*

. . . Den — he know it's a-*bendin' down over him*
— en he cain't skasely git his breath!

Den — den — he seem to feel someth'n *c-o-l-d,*
right down 'most agin his head! . . .

Den de voice say, *right at his year*
—"W-h-o — g-o-t — m-y — g-o-l-d-e-n — *arm?*

YOU'VE GOT IT!"

THE ROLLER COASTER
by William Fellows, Grade 6
Greenvale School, Eastchester

A roller coaster goes blink blink blink blast! Then it goes down very fast and round and round upside down hey! how long I lasts!

HOW THE CAMEL GOT HIS HUMP

Story by Rudyard Kipling, art by Willi Baum.

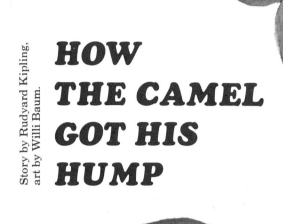

Humph!

In the beginning of years,
  when the world was so new-and-all,
   and the Animals were just
    beginning to work for Man,
     there was a Camel,
      and he lived in the middle of a Howling Desert
      because he did not want to work; and besides,
      he was a Howler himself.
    So he ate sticks and thorns
   and tamarisks and milkweed and prickles,
  most excruciating idle; and when anybody spoke
to him he said "*Humph!*" Just "*Humph!*"
and no more.

Presently the Horse came to him on Monday morning, with a saddle on his back and a bit in his mouth, and said, "Camel, O Camel, come out and trot like the rest of us."

"*Humph!*" said the Camel; and the Horse went away and told the Man.

Presently the Dog came to him, with a stick in his mouth, and said, "Camel, O Camel, come and fetch and carry like the rest of us."

"*Humph!*" said the Camel, and the Dog went away and told the Man.

Presently the Ox came to him, with the yoke on his neck, and said, "Camel, O Camel, come and plough like the rest of us."

"*Humph!*" said the Camel, and the Ox went away and told the Man.

At the end of the day
the Man called the Horse and the Dog and the Ox together,
and said, "Three, O Three, I'm very sorry for you
(with the world so new-and-all);
but that Humph-thing in the Desert can't work,
or he would have been here by now,
so I am going to leave him alone,
and you must work double-time to make up for it."

That made the Three very angry
(with the world so new-and-all),
and they held a palaver, and an *indaba*, and a *punchayet*,
and a pow-wow on the edge of the Desert;
and the Camel came chewing milkweed
most excruciating idle, and laughed at them.
Then he said

Humph!

and went away again.

Presently there came along the Djinn in charge of All Deserts,
rolling in a cloud of dust
(Djinns always travel that way because it is Magic),
and he stopped to palaver and pow-wow with the Three.
"Djinn of All Deserts," said the Horse,
"*is* it right for any one to be idle,
with the world so new-and-all?"
"Certainly not," said the Djinn.
"Well," said the Horse,
"there's a thing in the middle of your Howling Desert
(and he's a Howler himself)
with a long neck and long legs,
and he hasn't done a stroke of work
since Monday morning. He won't trot."
"Whew!" said the Djinn, whistling,
"that's my Camel, for all the gold in Arabia!
What does he say about it?"
"He says 'Humph!'" said the Dog;
"and he won't fetch and carry."
"Does he say anything else?"
"Only 'Humph!'; and he won't plough," said the Ox.
"Very good," said the Djinn.
"I'll humph him if you will kindly wait a minute."
The Djinn rolled himself up in his dust-cloak,
and took a bearing across the Desert,
and found the Camel most excruciatingly idle,
looking at his own reflection in a pool of water.

"My long and bubbling friend," said the Djinn,
"what's this I hear of your doing no work,
with the world so new-and-all?"
"*Humph!*" said the Camel.
The Djinn sat down, with his chin in his hand,
and began to think a Great Magic,
while the Camel looked at his own reflection in the pool of water.
"You've given the Three extra work ever since Monday morning,
all on account of your excruciating idleness," said the Djinn;
and he went on thinking Magics, with his chin in his hand.
"*Humph!*" said the Camel.

"I shouldn't
    say that again
        if I were you," said the Djinn;
        "you might say it once too often.
            Bubbles, I want you to work."
            And the Camel said "*Humph!*" again;

        but no sooner had he said it
        than he saw his back,
    that he was so proud of,
     puffing up and puffing up
      into a great big
      lolloping
      humph.

"Do you see that?" said the Djinn.
"That's your very own humph
that you've brought
upon your very own self
by not working.
To-day is Thursday,
and you've done no work since Monday,
when the work began.
Now you are going to work."
"How can I," said the Camel,
"with this humph on my back?"
"That's made a-purpose," said the Djinn,
"all because you missed those three days.
You will be able to work now
for three days without eating,
because you can live on your humph;
and don't you ever say
I never did anything for you.
Come out of the Desert
and go to the Three,
and behave.
Humph yourself!"

And the Camel humphed himself, humph and all,
and went away to join the Three. And from that day to this the Camel
always wears a humph (we call it "hump" now, not to hurt his feelings):
but he has never yet caught up with the three days
that he missed at the beginning of the world,
and he has never yet learned how to behave.

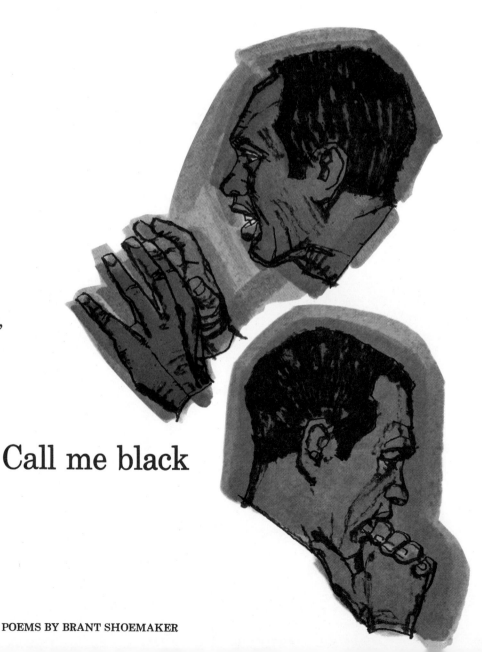

Call me
Black—
No, not
Black-hearted or
Black of
Despair but
Black of
Ebony,
Shiny and
Good,
Black of
Mahogany,
Solid but
Soft and
Warm to the
Touch.

Call me
Not
Black of
Midnight,
Distant and
Cold, but
Black velvet
Night of
Envelopment,
Delicate and
Rich.
Call me
Black and
Beautiful.
I am
Black.
I am
Beautiful.
Hear my
Song,
Black child,
Black and
Beautiful
Child!

Call me black

POEMS BY BRANT SHOEMAKER

Love and wrath

Let us
All be
Deeply
Men and
Women of
Love and
Wrath,
Kindling with
Might of
Dreams
Thundering
Yellow
Flames to
Char
Brute
Bigotry
To an
Ash,
And yet with
Gentle hands
Lead children
Far from
Such a
Stench,
Tomorrow's child
Asking,
"What is
War and
Prej-a-dis?"
Our
Answer being,
"Things of
Long ago—
Dragons,
Trolls and
Witches'
Brews."

Lions

Says the black man:
I mean, that was
Class, man,
Being fed to the
Lions and all that
Jazz.
Class, man,
Class.
But these same
Christians, man,
Is feedin'
Me to the
Dogs.
"Sic 'em, boy,
Sic 'em!"
I mean,
Give me the
Romans, man,
Every time.
Just any time you
Say.

229

DRAWINGS BY CHARLES BREY

Seaweed

BY SUSAN HAZELTON,
PHOTOGRAPH BY SCOTTY SAPIRO

Here is a photograph of my favorite species of seaweed,
which I gathered at the ocean's edge
near Seattle one morning.
It was photographed by a friend who is a commercial photographer.
Isn't it delicately beautiful?
Its scientific name is *rhodoptilum plumosum*,
a species of red algae (or seaweed)
whose magnificent form is rarely seen. Its unusual color
is due to the presence within its cells
of special red and blue pigments called *phycobilins*.
These pigments enable the plant to use, for photosynthesis,
those wavelengths of light
which can penetrate the sea water to the five to ten fathom depth
at which it usually grows. Here the light is so dim
that even a scuba diver may have trouble
seeing *rhodoptilum's* delicate outline among the rocks
and wood and coarser forms of seaweed on the ocean floor.
Although it is usually collected for scientific purposes by dredging,
it is occasionally found washed up on nearby beaches after a storm.
Then it looks like nothing more than a reddish brown blob
until placed in water where its branches can spread out.
The area along the United States and Canadian Pacific Coasts
where this species grows is very limited,
but other finely patterned forms of red, green or brown algae
can often be found in the tangled mass
washed in with the tide,
or growing on rocks exposed at low tide.

231

The Arrow and the Song

A POEM BY HENRY W. LONGFELLOW

I shot an arrow into the air,
It fell to earth, I know not where;
For, so swiftly it flew, the sight
Could not follow it in its flight.

I breathed a song into the air,
It fell to earth, I know not where;
For who has sight so keen and strong
That he can follow the flight of song?

Long, long afterward, in an oak
I found the arrow, still unbroke;
And the song, from beginning to end,
I found again in the heart of a friend.

232

God's World

A POEM BY EDNA ST. VINCENT MILLAY

O world, I cannot hold thee close enough!
    Thy winds, thy wide gray skies!
    Thy mists that roll and rise!
Thy woods, this autumn day, that ache and sag
And all but cry with color! That gaunt crag
To crush! To lift the lean of that black bluff!
World, world, I cannot get thee close enough!

Long have I known a glory in it all,
    But never knew I this;
    Here such a passion is
As stretcheth me apart. Lord, I do fear
Thou'st made the world too beautiful this year.
My soul is all but out of me, — let fall
No burning leaf; prithee, let no bird call.

BIG JOHN,

BIG JOHN,

g Cooper - 66

A SONG BY JIMMY DEAN,
PAINTING BY JEANNE COOPER

Words and music by Jimmy Dean.
Copyright 1961
by Fred Rose Music, Inc.
Used by permission of the publisher.

Every morning at the mine you could see him arrive,
He stood six-foot-six and weighed two-forty-five.
Kind of broad at the shoulder and narrow at the hip,
And everybody knew you didn't give no lip to BIG JOHN!

BIG JOHN - BIG BAD JOHN, BIG JOHN.

Nobody seemed to know where John called home,
He just drifted into town and stayed all alone.
He didn't say much, a-kinda quiet and shy,
And if you spoke at all, you just said, "Hi" to BIG JOHN!

Somebody said he came from New Orleans,
Where he got in a fight over a Cajun queen.
And a crashing blow from a huge right hand
Sent a Louisiana fellow to the promised land. BIG JOHN!

BIG JOHN - BIG BAD JOHN, BIG JOHN.

Then came the day at the bottom of the mine
When a timber cracked and the men started crying.
Miners were praying and hearts beat fast,
And everybody thought that they'd breathed their last 'cept John.
Through the dust and the smoke of this man-made hell
Walked a giant of a man that the miners knew well.
Grabbed a sagging timber and gave out with a groan,
And, like a giant oak tree, just stood there alone. BIG JOHN!

BIG JOHN, BIG JOHN - BIG BAD JOHN, BIG JOHN.

And with all of his strength, he gave a mighty shove;
Then a miner yelled out, "There's a light up above!"
And twenty men scrambled from a would-be grave,
And now there's only one left down there to save BIG JOHN!

With jacks and timbers they started back down
Then came that rumble way down in the ground,
And smoke and gas belched out of that mine,
Everybody knew it was the end of the line for BIG JOHN!

BIG JOHN, BIG JOHN - BIG BAD JOHN, BIG JOHN.

Now they never re-opened that worthless pit,
They just placed a marble stand in front of it;
These few words are written on that stand:
"At the bottom of this mine lies a big, big man; BIG JOHN!"

BIG JOHN, BIG JOHN - BIG BAD JOHN, BIG JOHN.

You must be joking!

DRAWING BY GERALD LYNAS

237

Noah
A CHORAL READING,
BY HARRY BELEFONTE AND BILL ATTAWAY

SOLO 1	Brothers
UNISON	Yes?
SOLO 1	Sisters
UNISON	Yes?
SOLO 1	It says here in Genesis one Chapter one
UNISON	One Chapter one
SOLO 1	In the beginning GOD made the earth
UNISON	Yah
SOLO 1	It also says here in Genesis six Chapter six
UNISON	Six Chapter six
SOLO 1	That the children of Israel were sinning
UNISON	Sinning
SOLO 1	That's exactly what I said. And when God saw them sinning *(quietly begin to build)* It hurt him to his heart And hurt him so bad it made him mad Made him so angry the skies got dark. And it was then he told Noah to build the ark
SOLO 1	Who built the ark?
UNISON	Noah!
SOLO 1	Who built the ark?
UNISON	Noah
SOLO 1	Who built the ark?
UNISON	Noah, Noah Noah built that ark

SOLO 1	Children stop and kneel and listen to me
	God walked down by the finest sea
	And he said evil of the sinful man
	Declared that he would destroy the land
	Spoke to Noah but Noah stopped
	He said, "Look here Noah
	Build me an ark."
	Want you to build it big and strong
	Build it 300 cubic long
	30 high about 50 wide
	I want it to stand my rain and tide.

GROUP C   O'er this day I'll make my mark
In a hundred years I want that ark.
When I get through with this evil land
Not a living thing is gonna stand

Except the things that I tell to you
That I'm gonna need when the world is new
I've been East and I've been West
And I've decided to put this world at rest.

GROUP B   I've been up and I've been down
And I've seen evil all around.
I've seen brother sin against brother!

UNISON   And I've decided it will go no further *(violently)*
Women weep and children mourn *(quietly)*
Sorry the day that man was born.
Sinful people one by one

SOLO 1   Sorry the day my wrath begun
Sorry the day my wrath begun
Because it's gonna rain

GROUP B   Because it's gonna rain

GROUP C   Because it's gonna rain

GROUP A   Because it's gonna rain

SOLO	'Cause all this land is my land Not a living thing is gonna stand For it's gonna rain
GROUP B	It's gonna rain
GROUP B & C	It's gonna rain
GROUP A, B, C	It's gonna rain
UNISON	It's gonna rain
SOLO 1	Who built the ark?
UNISON	Noah
SOLO 1	Who built the ark?
UNISON	Noah
SOLO 1	Noah built the ark.
UNISON	Now God told him what to do And brother Noah began to cut and hew Swinging his hammer with judgment With the singing of the saw, God said
SOLO 1	"Repent."

UNISON	For 100 years he hammered and saw'd Building the ark by the grace of God. After the foundation was laid He put down the timber and the ark was made.
GROUP B	Called in the animals two by two
GROUP C	There was the ox, the camel, and the kangaroo
GROUP A	The elephant, the monkey, and the crocodile,
GROUP B	The little bitty animals that couldn't smile.
GROUP C	He had them in the ark so tight The owl couldn't get no sleep at night.
GROUP A	The golden leopard hand in hand
SOLO	And God began to flood the land He raised his hands from heaven on high And knocked the sun and moon from the sky,
GROUP C	Shook the mountains, stirred the sea,
GROUP A	Hitched his wings to a chariot wheel, Stepped on the land and stood on the shore
SOLO	Glad good times to be no more 'Cause it's gonna rain.
UNISON	'Cause it's gonna rain *(softer)*
GROUP C	'Cause it's gonna rain *(softer)*
GROUP B	'Cause it's gonna rain *(very soft)*

THE GHOSTLY HITCHHIKER

a folktale retold by Ken Williams,
photographs by Joel Weltman

It was a dark night in the canyon.
Rain fell in heavy gusts
making driving difficult.

The headlights of a lone car
pierced the thickness.
A couple was headed
for San Francisco.

The woman sat peering out
at the dark shapes
of trees and bushes
that lined the road,
helping her husband watch against
the dangers of the twisting trail.

"John, this place gives me the creeps."

"We'll be out of the canyon
in a few minutes, Edna.
Then it will be
a good straight highway
the rest of the way home."

As the car rounded a curve,
the headlights picked up
. . . something . . .
a figure . . . a young girl . . .
waving wildly
from the side of the road.

243

"John, there's a girl up ahead!
What, in heaven's name,
is she doing out on a night like this?"

As John slowed the car and stopped,
the beam of the headlights illuminated the girl.
She came toward the car,
a thankful look on her face.
She wore a white dress . . . a cheery party dress
now limp and shapeless from the rain.
She appeared to be seventeen or eighteen.
Her long hair hung in dripping wet strands.
She clutched a small bunch of roses.

"Need a ride?"
John shouted to be heard
above the roar of wind and rain.

"Yes, please," said the girl.

"We're going into San Francisco."

Edna opened the door and leaned ahead,
pulling the back rest of her seat forward
to allow the girl to get in the rear seat of the sedan.
"You poor child, you're soaked to the skin.
Here, take this blanket and wrap up in it."

John put the car in gear and continued along the deserted road.

"Where you headed?" he asked.

"San Francisco."

"Well, you're in luck.
That's where we're going," Edna said.
"Do you live there?"

After a long silence . . . "Yes."

"Where in the City do you live, dear?"

Another silence. "1010 Sutter Street."

"That not too far out of our way, is it, John?" Edna said.

"No. We go right by there."

By this time they had left the canyon behind
and were picking up speed heading across the flat land toward the city.
The rain had slackened.
The girl dozed off
and Edna sat silently watching the road, wondering —
Who was the girl?
Where had she been?
What was she doing on the canyon road?

She tried to piece together all the details:
She lives in San Francisco . . .
in her late teens . . .
wearing a party dress . . .
carrying flowers . . .

It now had stopped raining.

The car continued toward the city, motor humming,
tires whining on the wet highway.
No one spoke.

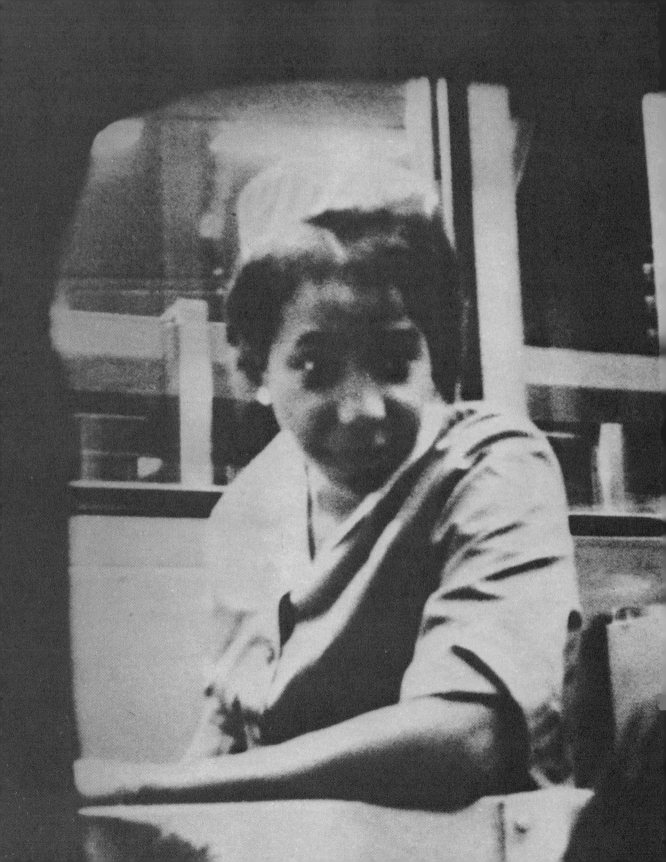

The car neared the Dumbarton Bridge,
a low, narrow structure
which spans the southern tip of San Francisco Bay.

John slowed the car,
carefully approaching the brightly lighted toll plaza.
He stopped beside the toll booth
and rolled down his window.

The guard stepped from the booth
and reached out her hand, "How many?"

John fished some coins from his pocket.
He started to say "Two,"
when he remembered his extra passenger.
"Uh — three.
I almost forgot about the girl in the back seat."

The guard moved closer and peered into the car.
"What girl?
There's no girl back there."

John and Edna both spun around
and stared at the back seat.
It was empty.
Only the rumpled, empty blanket lay on the seat,
illuminated by the blueish fluorescent lights
slanting in from the toll plaza.

"But — she was there!
We picked her up in the canyon!
Where did she go?" John managed to say,
partly to the guard
but mostly to voice his own disbelief.

"Look, mister, I've had people try to *hide* passengers,
but you're the first who's tried to *invent* one.
If I didn't think you were joking,
I'd have you take a sobriety test.
Now, you'd better move along;
I don't feel like playing games tonight."

Mechanically, John handed the coins to the guard
and drove forward toward the bridge.
Its string of lights stretched across the bay.

For awhile neither John nor Edna spoke.
The bottom had dropped out of reality.

Was the girl a figment of their imagination?
Not likely.

Had the girl somehow left through one of the back windows?
Surely they would have heard something.

Did the girl have some strange power of hypnotism?
Hardly possible.

Each question led to a blank.

Soon they left the bridge behind
and turned north on U.S. 101,
the major freeway leading to San Francisco.
It felt comforting to be on a wide highway
with other cars.

Still, now and then,
Edna would glance back furtively
to make sure the rear seat was still empty.

The closer they got to the city limits,
the more fearful Edna became.
She knew her husband.
He was one
who could not leave a problem unanswered
once he became involved with it.
He would be determined
to go directly to the address the girl gave.
She knew it.
But she asked anyway,
"Where are you going?"

"To 1010 Sutter Street."

"What do you think you'll find?
There may not even *be* such a place."

"I realize that.
But I've got to know.
There has to be some explanation for this whole crazy episode.
The address is the only clue we have."

Edna found herself hoping
that the address would be nonexistent,
or a vacant lot.
By now her usual curiosity was completely smothered
by her fear of the unknown.

Before long they were on Sutter.
John eased the car along, counting off the numbers.

Suddenly there it was.
The address the girl had given.
The porch light was on,
as though visitors were expected.

John pulled the car to the curb and stopped.
He looked over at his wife.
"Are you coming?" he said calmly.

Edna hesitated.
She was afraid to go,
and yet she was afraid to stay.
She slowly opened the car door and followed.

They walked up the steps,
rang the doorbell, and waited.

The door opened.

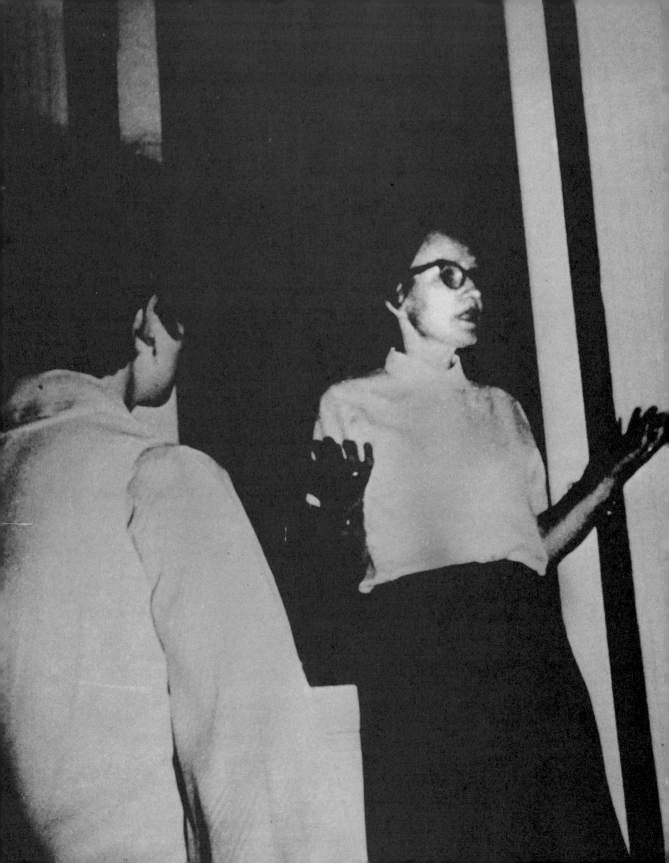

Standing there, framed in the doorway,
was a middle-aged woman.
"Yes?" she said.

John introduced himself and his wife.
Then he began, telling
about the bewildering encounter with
the girl in the white dress.
"Before she disappeared,
the girl said that she lived at this address.
Do you know *anything* about the girl?"

The woman listened solemnly.
Then she spoke, her voice beyond suffering,
her eyes beyond tears:
"Yes, that was my daughter.
She was killed in an automobile accident in Niles Canyon
ten years ago tonight, February 26.
Since then, every year on this date,
I have had a caller who relates the same story you just told.
You are the tenth."
She closed the door without another word.

John and Edna walked back to the car, puzzled and sad.
"You didn't believe that woman, did you, John?
She's likely out of her head
over the loss of her daughter.
Grief does that sometimes to people."

"You're probably right, Edna," John said.
Then, as he opened the car door,
he noticed something on the rear floor.

It was a bouquet of flowers, still fresh . . .
ten red roses.

Somewhere, far out in the bay, a lonely foghorn sounded.

The Love and Marriage of a Mouse

A FOLKSONG, PICTURES BY CHARLES BREY

There was a frog lived in a spring,
Twiddle, widdle, widdle, widdle, widdle,
Widdle, widdle, wing.
He was so hoarse he could not sing,
Twiddle, widdle, widdle, widdle, widdle,
Widdle, widdle, wing.

He took a swig of sassy-fras tea,
Twiddle, widdle, widdle, widdle, widdle,
Widdle, widdle, wee.
And then his song was fine and free,
Twiddle, widdle, widdle, widdle, widdle,
Widdle, widdle, wee.

He courted a mouse and her name was Bess,
Twiddle, widdle, widdle, widdle, widdle,
Widdle, widdle, wess.
And he courted and courted till she said, "Yes,"
Twiddle, widdle, widdle, widdle, widdle,
Widdle, widdle, wess.

Her Maw and Paw says, "Frogs ain't nice!"
Twiddle, widdle, widdle, widdle, widdle,
Widdle, widdle, wice.
She said, "They're quite as nice as mice,"
Twiddle, widdle, widdle, widdle, widdle,
Widdle, widdle, wice.

They got married, folks do tell,
Twiddle, widdle, widdle, widdle, widdle,
Widdle, widdle, well.
And they lived at the bottom of the old green well,
Twiddle, widdle, widdle, widdle, widdle,
Widdle, widdle, well.

Then Mousie waded in water to her chin,
Twiddle, widdle, widdle, widdle, widdle,
Widdle, widdle, win.
And she often wished she was single again,
Twiddle, widdle, widdle, widdle, widdle,
Widdle, widdle, win.

A Dollar's Worth (of Seed)

AS TOLD BY PAUL WILLIAMS TO BOBBY MCGUIRE, ART BY RAY BARBER

Years ago, Martha Berry thought and dreamed
about starting a school for young orphan girls.
In 1902, she founded Berry School in Rome, Georgia.
Today the institution is called Berry College.

At the beginning,
Mrs. Berry's funds for the school were very limited.
The school was facing financial trouble
so she decided to write handwritten letters
to prominent, wealthy businessmen and ask for their help.

One of the men to whom she wrote was Henry Ford,
founder of Ford Motor Company in Detroit.

Henry Ford answered her letter and told her
he appreciated what she was doing
for such a worthy cause.
He enclosed a check for $1.00.

If you had been Martha Berry,
how would you have reacted to receiving a check for $1.00
from a wealthy man who represented
one of America's largest companies?

Martha Berry did some thinking and then went to work.

She selected a small piece of land on the school grounds
and named it the Henry Ford Garden.
She bought seeds with the dollar and planted them there.

During harvest time that year
several of the young girls were working in the garden
and Mrs. Berry got her camera and took a picture
of the girls harvesting the vegetables.
Mr. Henry Ford's dollar had been put to work —
and was producing dividends.

A few days later,
Mrs. Berry wrote another letter to Henry Ford.
This time she enclosed a picture
of the girls harvesting the vegetables.

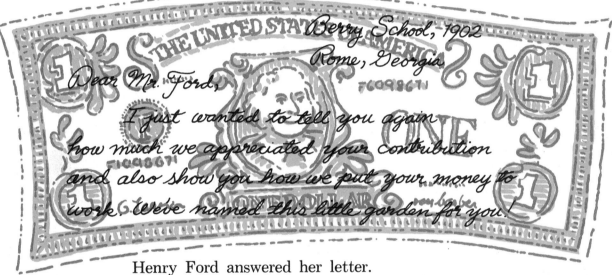

Berry School, 1902
Rome, Georgia

Dear Mr. Ford,

I just wanted to tell you again
how much we appreciated your contribution
and also show you how we put your money to
work. We've named this little garden for you!

Henry Ford answered her letter.
He thanked her for her letter and the picture.
He was pleased and touched.

*Please continue the out standing work you are
doing with your young ladies.*

His last paragraph indicated
that he was enclosing another check
for the school.

The check was for $1,000,000 . . .

RENÉ MAGRITTE - LA POITRINE, COLLECTION R. SCAIFE, PITTSBURGH

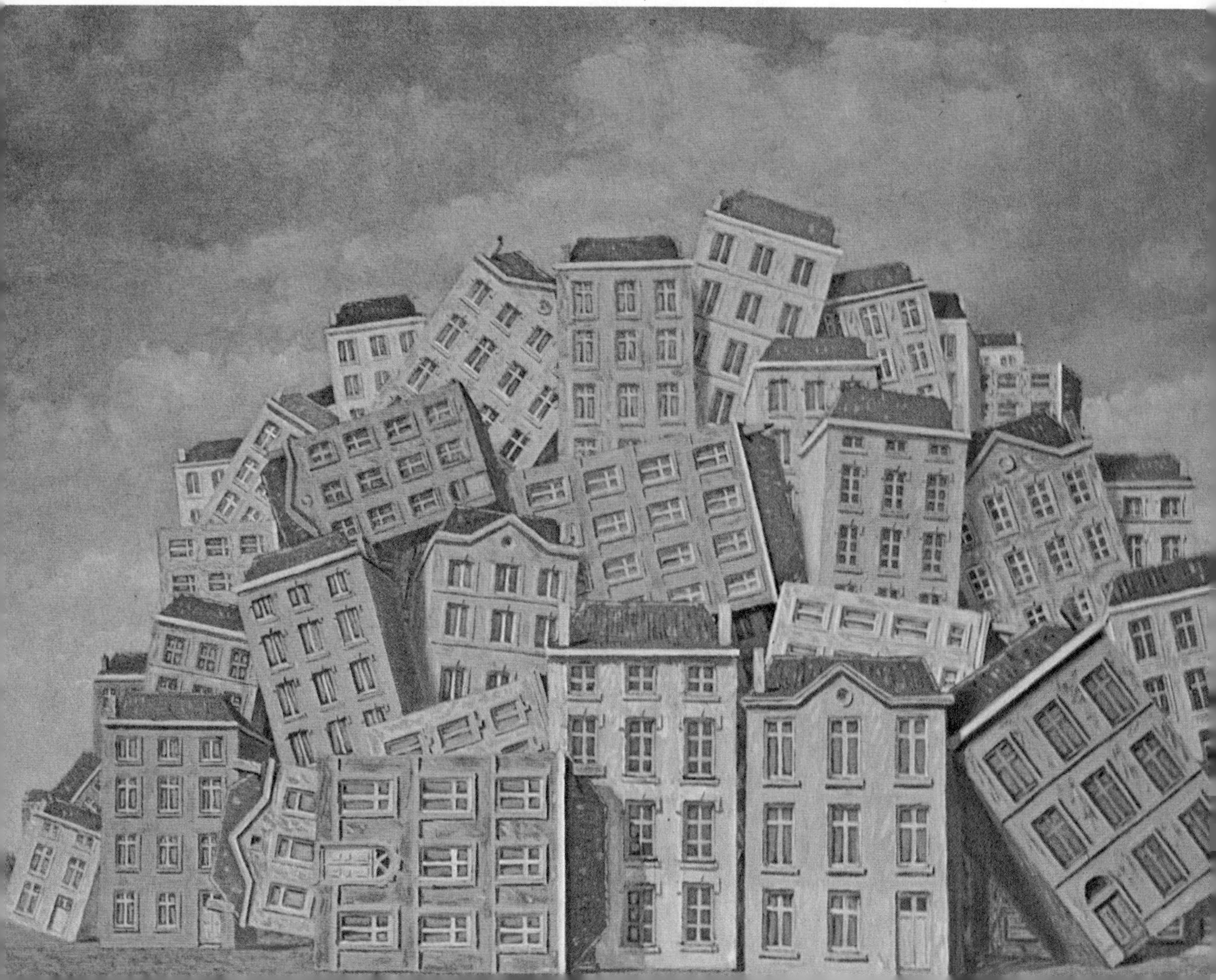

Sonic Boom

A POEM BY JOHN UPDIKE

I'm sitting in the living room,
When, up above, the Thump of Doom
Resounds. Relax. It's sonic boom.

The ceiling shudders at the clap,
The mirrors tilt, the rafters snap,
And Baby wakens from his nap.

"Hush, babe. Some pilot we equip,
Giving the speed of sound the slip,
Has cracked the air like a penny whip."

Our world is far from frightening; I
No longer strain to read the sky
Where moving fingers (jet planes) fly.
Our world seems much too tame to die.

And if it does, with one more pop,
I shan't look up to see it drop.

A Road Down in the Sea

A story by Lorenz Graham, pictures by Gregorio Prestopino

The Egypt people hold the Hebrews tight
And make them slaves
And make them work the farm
And work the road
And work some kind of hard.
The Hebrews cry
And sometimes they fall down and die
And all the time they moan and pray
And say "How long, O God, how long?"

God see the thing.
He hear Him people pray
And so He raise up Moses and He say
  "Moses,
    You the one
    To go fore Old King Pharoah.
    You the one to carry him My Word.
    Tell King Pharoah that I say
    'Let My people go!
    Tell him,
    'Let My people go!' "
King Pharoah no want hear that Word
But God put Him hand there
And take the Hebrews out.
He take them all,
The mens, the womens,
The old ones and the young.
He take them out from Egypt land
He start them back to Canaan
And Moses be they leader.

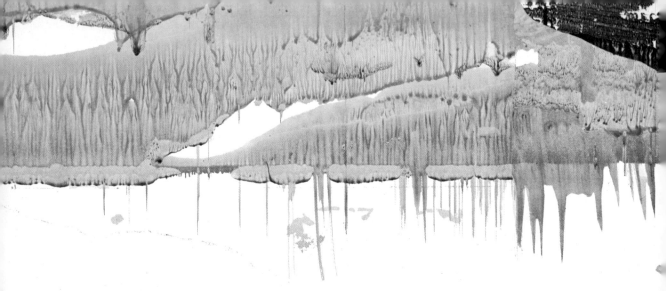

Now Moses never see that side before
And he don't know the way.
God say

"Moses,
Nev mind.
I set My mark up in the sky
You walk the way I show.
By day My mark be in a cloud
By night it be in fire."
And so they follow day by day
Across the sea of sand
And on the mountains
And in bush and swamp.

And they be plenty.

King Pharoah come along behind
With all him army to make war
To take the Hebrews back for slaves again.
They come up close.
The Hebrews move out fast at night.
The soldiers come again.
The Hebrews move by day and night.
The soldiers come some more.
The Hebrews fear and run and then they reach a sea,
They reach a sea they no can cross.

They stop and cry.

   "How now?" they say.

"How now?

   Moses done bring we here to die.

   We no can swim

   We no can find canoe

   We no can ride a steamer.

   How now?"

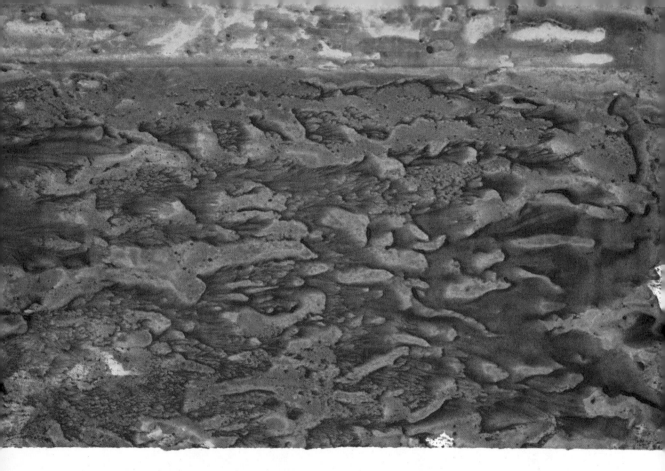

They cry and Moses self he fear
But Moses pray.
Now God can fix up anything.
God say
   "Moses, wait!
     I show who rule the land and water
     I show the people who can save them
     I show all people who the true God be.
     Wait!"
And Moses wait.

God say
   "Make the people
     meet Me on the beach!"
Moses do so.

God say
   "Moses.
     Hold out your stick,
     Hold it out over the water."
Moses do so.

Softly, softly east wind rise to blow.
It blow soft but with a force from God
And while the people look
They see the waters move.
Some water move one side and some the other
Some turn about and move and some move straight
Some move slow and some move quick
Some move in and some move out
Some come some go
But all do move.

While the people look
The waters open up and make a road down in the sea
While on two sides it rise and stand like mountains.
God say
   "Go!
      And while you go
      I will go with you!"

271

The people fear to go
But Moses lead
And one man go behind
Then two, then three, then plenty more,
And all the people follow through
And no man wet him foot.
When Pharoah come he see the road
He see the Hebrews marching on.
He never see such thing before
He don't know God.

He say
  "I too will go
    And on the other side
    I take the Hebrew people.
    March!"
The Army march.

273

They come on down the road
They no get wet till all the army march
With water high on one side and the other.
Then God reach down
And lay small trouble in the way
And men fall down and horses turn about.
The army stop.
The drummers beat they drums
The leaders call
The head men shout
The horn men blow they horns.
The king cry out.
Moses look down the road on the other side.
God speak softly to him.
Moses bow him head
He lift him stick
The waters go to move again
And water mountains fall and roll
And men cry out

While waves run high
And all the waters move about
Like they be vex.

And bye-m-bye a wave bring up King Pharoah dead
And lay him down
At Moses foot.

Ten Billion, Ten Million

10, 010, 010, 010
Is a number so grand
You say it again:
10, 010, 010, 010!

10, 010, 010, 010
Is a number so superly fine,
But I'd like to point out it's only one more than—
10, 010, 010, 009!

A VERSE BY PHIL KEILS

278

Ten Thousand and Ten

Inside the

AN OLD SONG

She sailed away
on a happy summer day
on the back of a crocodile;
"You see," said she,
"He's as tame as he can be,
I'll ride him down the Nile."
The croc winked his eye
as he bade them all goodbye,
wearing a happy smile;

at the end of the ride
the lady was inside
of the smile on the crocodile.

BROOM HILDA®

THERE AIN'T MANY TROLLS AROUND, ARE THERE, IRWIN?

NO.

"BUT **ONCE**, GREAT HERDS OF TROLLS ROAMED THE VAST PRAIRIES OF MID-AMERICA. THEY NUMBERED IN THE MILLIONS..."

"OLD-TIMERS SAID THAT THE DUST CLOUDS FROM THOSE HERDS ACTUALLY BLOTTED OUT THE SUN!"

"THEY LIVED AND MULTIPLIED HAPPILY UNTIL THE TRAGIC YEAR OF 1839. THAT WAS THE YEAR OF THE GREAT HAIR TONIC STORMS. IT RAINED HAIR TONIC 40 DAYS AND 40 NIGHTS!"

"THIS CAUSED EXCESSIVE HAIR GROWTH. STAGGERING UNDER THE WEIGHT OF THIS EXTRA HAIR THEY DROPPED AND DIED BY THE MILLIONS."

"IN A LAST DESPERATE ATTEMPT TO SAVE THE GREAT HERDS, THE GOVERNMENT SENT IN THOUSANDS OF BARBERS. BUT, SADLY, IT WAS TOO LATE."

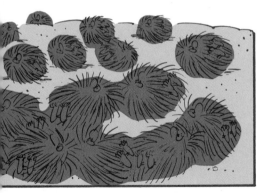

A CARTOON BY RUSSELL MYERS
Reprinted through the courtesy of the Chicago
Tribune-New York News Syndicate, Inc.

Loveliest of Trees

BY A. E. HOUSMAN, PAINTING BY CHEN CHI

Loveliest of trees, the cherry now
Is hung with bloom along the bough,
And stands about the woodland ride
Wearing white for Eastertide.

Now, of my threescore years and ten,
Twenty will not come again,
And take from seventy springs a score,
It only leaves me fifty more.

And since to look at things in bloom
Fifty springs are little room
About the woodlands I will go
To see the cherry hung with snow.

NO NEWS

AN ANECDOTE TOLD BY NAT M. WILLS

There was a man who was ordered by his physician
to go away to the mountains for a rest.
He went home, told the members of his family what the doctor had said,
and said, "While I am away I don't want to be annoyed
by phone calls or telegrams,
in fact I don't want to receive any news of any kind."

So he went away and was gone for about six weeks.
He returned to the city very much improved in health
and very anxious for some news from home.
He got off the train at the depot
and was met by his faithful servant,
and the following conversation ensued:

He said, "Well, Henry, how is everything at home?
Is there any news?"

Henry said, "No, sir, there ain't no news, sir,
everything is just about the same as when you all went away."

"Nothing happened?"

"No, sir, there ain't no news, sir,
there ain't nothin' to tell you, sir.
Except one little thing.
Since you went away, your dog died."

"My dog died, eh?
That's too bad.
What killed the dog?"

"Well, sir, the dog ate some burnt horseflesh
and that's what killed the dog."

"He ate burned horseflesh?
Where did he get burnt horseflesh to eat?"

"Well, sir, you know, your barn burnt down,
and after the fire the dog went in there
and ate some burnt horseflesh
and that's what killed the dog."

"Oh, my barn burned down, eh?"

"Oh, yes sir, yes indeed, sir,
the barn, that's all burnt down."

"Well, how did the barn catch fire?"

"Well, sir, you see, the sparks from the house
flew over and caught onto the barn,
burnt the barn down and burnt up
all the cows and the horses
and after the fire, the dog went in
and ate up some of the burnt horseflesh
and that's what killed the dog."

"Oh, so then my house burned down, too, eh?"

"Oh, yes sir, the house
it got completely destroyed."

"Well, how did the house catch fire?"

"Well sir, they had been
candles burnin' in the house,
and one of the candles
caught onto the curtains, and the curtains
caught onto the roof, and sparks flew over
and caught onto the barn
and burnt the barn down
and burnt up all the cows and the horses
and after the fire,
the dog went in
and ate up the burnt horseflesh
and that's what killed the dog."

"You mean, Henry,
you had candles burnin' in the house?

"Oh, yes sir, yes sir,
they had the candles there.
They had the candles
burnin' all 'round the coffin."

"Coffin? Whose dead?"

"Oh, yes sir, yes sir,
that's another little thing
I forgot to tell you about.
Since you been away
your mother-in-law died."

"Oh, my mother-in-law
died, eh?"

"Oh, yes sir, yes sir,
she's dead all right.
You needn't worry about that."

"Well, what killed
my mother-in-law?"

"Well, I don't know exactly
what killed her, sir.
But, around the neighborhood
they say it was from the shock
of your wife runnin' away
with the chauffeur.
But, outside of that, sir,
there ain't

"

AN APACHE GIRL COMES OF AGE

Text & photos by Arthur Sirdofsky

It's called the Apache Sunrise Dance, probably because it begins at dawn on each of three days. Winona Crawford, the Sunrise Girl, will dance till dusk each day as she and her family, together with Indians and a few whites from miles around, celebrate her becoming a woman. Winona's buckskin dress had been her mother's before and her grandmother's before that. It was part of the ritual that had to be perfect, right down to the last detail. Winona, with her cousin, are seen dancing on the first day. Behind them are chanting medicine men.

The three-day celebration is actually a rigorous ordeal for Winona — should she fall from exhaustion, she would fail to become a woman of the tribe. Part of the second day's ritual, involves the girl and the earth god. The girl works her way down into the sacred blanket, which serves as an intermediary between her and the earth, which symbolizes fertility. She is holding her hands out to the sun.

Now on the blanket, Winona is aided by relatives. They pace around her and press her close to the earth, thereby relaxing her and bringing her in closer contact with the earth god. Most of the men, some seen standing around the blanket, wear ordinary western-style clothes, though the women wear Indian camp dresses.

The devil dancers, however, have discarded their Levis and shirts in favor of the costumes that play an important role in the ritual. On part of the second day of the dance and most of the third, they swoop down out of the hills, wearing paint and black hoods, and wave sticks and rattles in the air. Their purpose is to scare away any lingering evil spirits and protect the young girl. This is also part of the preparation for the finale to Winona's ordeal.

Winona's father has just spread a white paste on her hair. This would be followed by members of the family and community sprinkling pollen on her, as a blessing and as the signal for the end of the dance.

Both Winona and her mother receive the blessing of the pollen from those that witnessed the dance. Each person scoops a handful of the yellow stuff and sprinkles it on their hair as they pass. Thus, the people are telling Winona not only that she has danced well, but that she is now a woman. The dance is over.

But the fun has just begun! Children signal the beginning of the festivities by diving into the baskets of fruit and candies that were assembled before the dance began. The feast includes cattle that are slaughtered and prepared at the end of the third day. When the festivities end, everyone pitches in to help clean up and dismantle temporary shelters that were erected for the duration of the dance.

Her only concern at the moment the man with the camera, this little girl tries to melt through her mother's dress. Her shyness will disappear in several years, though, for her time will come to dance the Apache Sunrise Dance. ♦

Crystal Moment

A POEM BY ROBERT P. TRISTRAM COFFIN

Once or twice this side of death
Things can make one hold his breath.

From my boyhood I remember
A crystal moment of September.

A wooded island rang with sounds
Of church bells in the throats of hounds.

A buck leaped out and took the tide
With jewels flowing past each side.

With his high head like a tree
He swam within a yard of me.

I saw the golden drop of light
In his eyes turned dark with fright.

I saw the forest's holiness
On him like a fierce caress.

Fear made him lovely past belief,
My heart was trembling like a leaf.

He leaned towards the land and life
With need above him like a knife.

In his wake the hot hounds churned,
They stretched their muzzles out
        and yearned.

They bayed no more, but swam
        and throbbed,
Hunger drove them till they sobbed.

Pursued, pursuers reached the shore
And vanished. I saw nothing more.

So they passed, a pageant such
As only gods could witness much,

Life and death upon one tether
And running beautiful together.

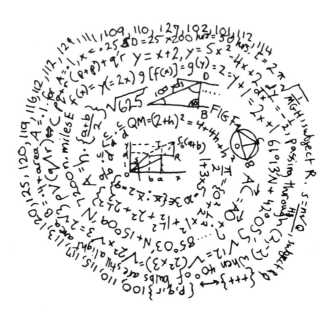

Brainstorm

A POEM BY ADRIAN LONGFORD (II)

An equation enters my reluctant head,
Competes for equality with the pencil I am gnawing,
And then it happens,
Unable to cope with the x's and y's,
My brain explodes,
Shatters inside my skull.
I try to regain the particles that have stuck in my eyes, ears, and nose,
Fragments of logic and knowledge all inside me.
Wait,
The answer is coming,
But it is wrong,
My shattered brain can no longer reason for itself,
The equation laughs to itself,
Its x's and y's and brackets cry out in merriment,
My tormented brain can stand it no longer,
The brainstorm rages on.

292

ice cream
i scream
ice cream

bright   blurred
chosen   rounded off
lucent   made indefinite
sharp   The side
                                                       nubbled
uneven   syrup-slow
curving   the image   the taste
but willed   the transformation   glyceride
jagged   the memory
                            eating it   smirched
silent   shimmering
magical, one   insatiable
moment only

melting   accumulating,
                                            dribbling, about
the shape itself   the cone   to drop
the texture   cardboard
a test   the surface
an admission   sticky as plastic

the recognition   immediate and
deceiving the mind   unknown
the lettering on the rim   trivial
arguing sugar crystals,   enormous
blatant, gummy, broken

the patchwork grill   licked
intensifying   moist
curving   still
                                 firm

outline   yet
curling its   dis-
fingers   appear-
around,   ing
and down

possessing

to draw, to take
in the hand,
to crunch
its one
point

Of Geese and Men

The goose was young, he couldn't fly,
And so was I.

We tried to learn, and learn we did,
Oh how we flew.

But geese and men return to earth
To age and die.

by John R. Dunn, *painting by Ted Rand*

FIRST FIGHT

A POEM BY VERNON SCANNELL,
ART BY HENRY MARKOWITZ

Tonight, then, is the night;
Stretched on the massage table,
Wrapped in his robe, he breathes
Liniment and sweat
And tries to close his ears
To the roaring of the crowd,
A murky sea of noise
That bears upon its tide
The frail sound of the bell
And brings the cunning fear
That he might not do well,
Not fear of bodily pain
But that his tight-lipped pride
Might be sent crashing down,
His white ambition slain,
Knocked spinning the glittering crown.
How could his spirit bear
That ignominious fall?
Not hero but a clown
Spurned or scorned by all.
The thought appals, and he
Feels sudden envy for
The roaring crowd outside
And wishes he were there
Anonymous and safe,
Calm in the tolerant air,
Would almost choose to be
Anywhere but here.

Nebuchadnezzar and the Fiery Furnace

AS TOLD IN THE THIRD CHAPTER OF DANIEL

Painting by Robert Shores, black and white art by Ray Barber

1 Nebuchadnezzar the king made an image of gold,
whose height *was* threescore cubits,
and the breadth thereof six cubits:
he set it up in the plain of Dura,
in the province of Babylon.

2 Then Nebuchadnezzar the king
sent to gather together
the princes, the governors, and the captains,
the judges, the treasurers, the counsellors, the sheriffs,
and all the rulers of the provinces,
to come to the dedication of the image
which Nebuchadnezzar the king had set up.

298

3 Then the princes, the governors, and captains,
the judges, the treasurers, the counsellors, the sheriffs,
and all the rulers of the provinces,
were gathered together
unto the dedication of the image
that Nebuchadnezzar the king had set up;
and they stood before the image
that Nebuchadnezzar had set up.

4 Then an herald cried aloud,
  To you it is commanded,
  O people, nations, and languages,

5 *That* at what time ye hear the sound of the cornet,
  flute, harp, sackbut, psaltery, dulcimer,
  and all kinds of musick,
  ye fall down and worship the golden image
  that Nebuchadnezzar the king hath set up:

6 And whoso falleth not down and worshippeth
  shall the same hour be cast
  into the midst of a burning fiery furnace.

7 Therefore at that time,
when all the people heard the sound of the cornet,
flute, harp, sackbut, psaltery, and dulcimer,
and all kinds of musick,
all the people, the nations, and the languages,
fell down *and* worshipped the golden image
that Nebuchadnezzar the king had set up.

8 Wherefore at that time
certain Chaldeans came near,
and accused the Jews.

9 They spake and said to the king Nebuchadnezzar,
O king, live for ever.

10 Thou, O king, hast made a decree,
that every man that shall hear the sound of the cornet,
flute, harp, sackbut, psaltery, and dulcimer,
and all kinds of musick,
shall fall down and worship the golden image:

11 And whoso falleth not down and worshippeth,
that he should be cast
into the midst of a burning fiery furnace.

12 There are certain Jews
whom thou hast set over the affairs
of the province of Babylon,
Shadrach, Meshach, and Abednego;
these men, O king,
have not regarded thee:
they serve not thy gods,
nor worship the golden image which thou hast set up.

13 Then Nebuchadnezzar in *his* rage and fury
commanded to bring Shadrach, Meshach, and Abednego.
Then they brought these men
before the king.

14 Nebuchadnezzar spake and said unto them,
Is it true, O Shadrach, Meshach, and Abednego,
do not ye serve my gods,
nor worship the golden image which I have set up?

15 Now if ye be ready
that at what time ye hear the sound of the cornet,
flute, harp, sackbut, psaltery, and dulcimer,
and all kinds of musick,
ye fall down and worship the image which I have made;
well:
but if ye worship not,
ye shall be cast the same hour
into the midst of a burning fiery furnace;
and who *is* that God
that shall deliver you out of my hands?

16 Shadrach, Meshach, and Abednego,
answered and said to the king,
O Nebuchadnezzar,
we *are* not careful
to answer thee in this matter.

17 If it be *so,*
our God whom we serve
is able to deliver us from the burning fiery furnace,
and he will deliver *us* out of thine hand,
O king.

18 But if not,
be it known unto thee O king,
that we will not serve thy gods,
nor worship the golden image which thou hast set up.

19 Then was Nebuchadnezzar full of fury,
and the form of his visage was changed against Shadrach,
Meshach, and Abednego:
therefore he spake,
and commanded that they should heat the furnace
one seven times more
than it was wont to be heated.

20 And he commanded the most mighty men
that *were* in his army
to bind Shadrach, Meshach, and Abednego,
and to cast *them* into the burning fiery furnace.

21 Then these men were bound in their coats,
their hosen, and their hats,
and their *other* garments,
and were cast into the midst
of the burning fiery furnace.

22 Therefore because the king's commandment was urgent,
and the furnace exceedingly hot,
the flame of the fire slew those men
that took up Shadrach, Meshach, and Abednego.

23 And these three men,
Shadrach, Meshach, and Abednego,
fell down bound
into the midst of the burning fiery furnace.

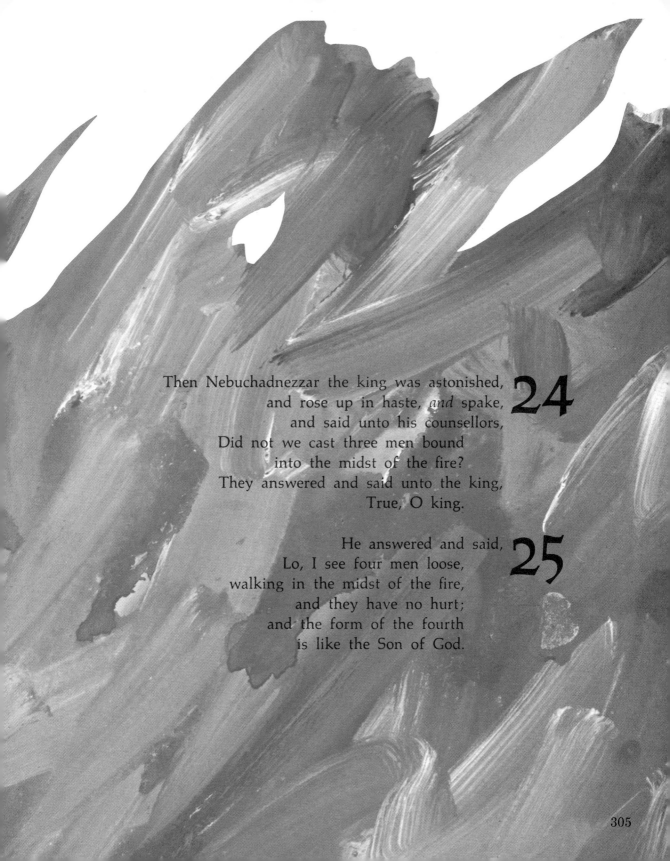

Then Nebuchadnezzar the king was astonished,
and rose up in haste, *and* spake,
and said unto his counsellors,
Did not we cast three men bound
into the midst of the fire?
They answered and said unto the king,
True, O king.

24

He answered and said,
Lo, I see four men loose,
walking in the midst of the fire,
and they have no hurt;
and the form of the fourth
is like the Son of God.

25

26 Then Nebuchadnezzar came near to the mouth
of the burning fiery furnace,
and spake,
and said,

> Shadrach, Meshach, and Abednego,
> ye servants of the most high God,
> come forth, and come *hither*.

Then Shadrach, Meshach, and Abednego,
came forth of the midst of the fire.

27 And the princes, governors, and captains,
and the king's counsellors, being gathered together,
saw these men,
upon whose bodies the fire had no power,
nor was an hair of their head singed,
neither were their coats changed,
nor had the smell of fire passed on them.

28 *Then* Nebuchadnezzar spake, and said,
Blessed *be* the God of Shadrach,
Meshach, and Abednego,
who hath sent his angel,
and delivered his servants that trusted in him,
and have changed the king's word,
and yielded their bodies,
that they might not serve nor worship any god,
except their own God.

29 Therefore I make a decree,
that every people, nation, and language,
which speak any thing amiss
against the God of Shadrach, Meshach, and Abednego,
shall be cut in pieces,
and their houses shall be made a dunghill:
because there is no other God
that can deliver after this sort.

30 Then the king promoted Shadrach,
Meshach, and Abednego,
in the province of Babylon.

309

A POEM BY WALTER DE LA MARE,
ILLUSTRATIONS BY ROBERT J. LEE

AS LUCY WENT A-WALKING

one morning cold and fine,
There sate three crows upon a bough,
and three times three are nine:
Then "O!" said Lucy, in the snow,
"it's very plain to see
A witch has been a-walking in the fields in front of me."

Then stept she light and heedfully across the frozen snow,
And plucked a bunch of elder-twigs that near a pool did grow;
And, by and by, she comes to seven shadows in one place
Stretched black by seven poplar-trees against the sun's bright face.

She looks to left, she looks to right, and in the midst she sees
    A little pool of water clear and frozen 'neath the trees;
    Then down beside its margent in the crusted snow she kneels,
    And hears a magic belfry, ringing with sweet bells.

Clear rang the faint far merry peal, then silence on the air,
And icy-still the frozen pool and poplars standing there:
Then, soft, as Lucy turned her head and looked along the snow
She sees a witch—a witch she sees, come frisking to and fro.

Her scarlet, buckled shoes they clicked, her heels a-twinkling high;
With mistletoe her steeple-hat bobbed as she capered by;
But never a dint, or mark, or print, in the whiteness there to see,
Though danced she light, though danced she fast, though danced she lissomely.

It seemed 'twas diamonds in the air, or tiny flakes of frost;
It seemed 'twas golden smoke around, or sunbeams lightly tossed;
It seemed an elfin music like to reeds' and warblers' rose:
"Nay!" Lucy said, "it is the wind that through the branches flows."

And as she peeps, and as she peeps, 'tis no more one, but three,
And eye of bat, and downy wing of owl within the tree,
And the bells of that sweet belfry a-pealing as before,
And now it is not three she sees, and now it is not four.

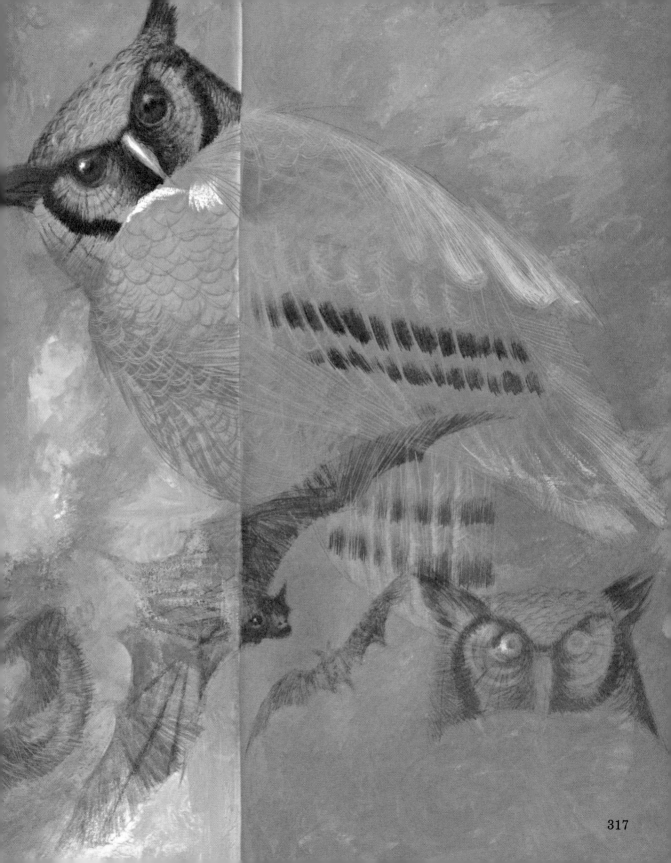

"O! who are ye,"
      sweet Lucy cries,
            "that in a dreadful ring,
All muffled up in brindled shawls,
      do caper, frisk, and spring?"
"A witch and witches,
      one and nine,"
           they straight to her reply,
And look upon her narrowly,
      with green and needle eye.

Then Lucy sees in clouds of gold
      sweet cherry trees upgrow,
And bushes of red roses
      that bloomed above the snow;
She smells all faint
      the almond-boughs
           blowing so wild and fair,
And doves with milky eyes ascend
      fluttering in the air.

Clear flowers she sees, like tulip buds, go floating by like birds,
 With wavering tips that warbled sweetly strange enchanted words;
 And as with ropes of amethyst the twigs with lamps were hung,
 And clusters of green emeralds like fruit upon them clung.

"O witches nine, ye dreadful nine, O witches three times three."
Whence come these wondrous things that I this Christmas morning see?"
But straight, as in a clap, when she of "Christmas" says the word,
Here is the snow, and there the sun, but never bloom nor bird;

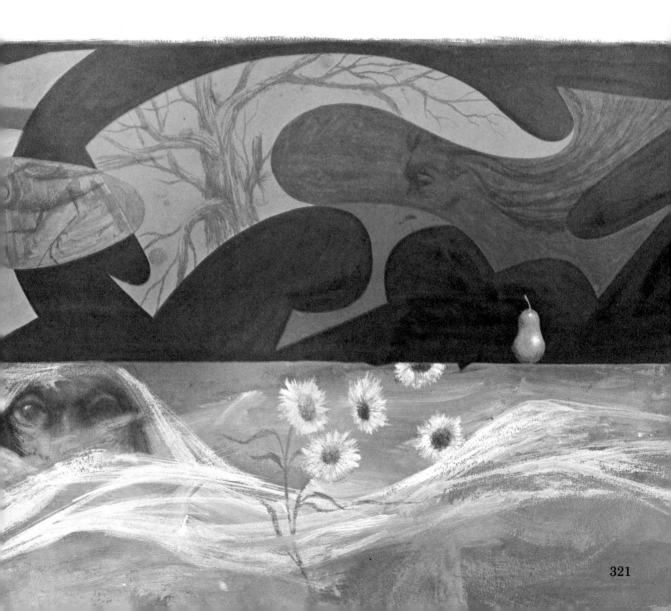

Nor warbling flame,
                    nor gloaming-rope
                              of amethyst there shows,
        Nor bunches of green emeralds,
                              nor belfry,
                                        well, and rose,
        Nor cloud of gold,
                    nor cherry-tree,
                              nor witch in brindled shawl,
        But like a dream which vanishes,
                    so vanished
                              were they all.

When Lucy sees,
                    and only sees
                              three crows upon a bough,
        And earthly twigs,
                    and brushes
                              hidden white in driven snow,
        Then "O!" said Lucy,
                    "three times three are nine
                              —I plainly see
        Some witch has been a-walking
                              in the fields in front of me."

CASEY STENGEL FRACTURED THE LANGUAGE

How Casey Stengel Got His Name

AN EXPLANATION BY CHARLES DILLON STENGEL,
HANDLETTERING BY RAY BARBER

Well, that's a very strange thing.
I was born in Kansas City, Missouri.
My parents were born in Davenport, Iowa.
And my mother and father were born in Rock Island, Illinois.
So, I started in Kansas City, where I was born,
and I went for years and years, as, uh,
under the name of Dutch Stengel,
and then we moved so many places in Kansas City,
and in each neighborhood you go in for,
they'd learn your name and look at you,
saw my name is Stengel, and it was a German name,
and then they'd call me, Dutch, Dutch, Dutch,
and then I went into baseball,
I went to Gangegill, Illinois
and they said, Where is your home town,
and I'd say Kansas City, Missouri.
So they kept callin' me Casey.
So, whether it was 'Casey,' or K and a C.
Then it got where I got up in the East,
and there were several writers

BUT YOU'LL ~~FIND YOURSELF~~ S
(ENJOY THE)

TRUGGE ~~ING~~ TO ~~GET THE~~ SENSE OUT
(L) (MAKE)

OF WHAT ~~THE~~ ˅ SAYS
(THIS FAMOUS BASEBALL PLAYER)
(˄)
(AND COACH)

and so many men who were writin' poems,
and the first baseball poem sold
that same out was "Strike Out, Casey."
And several times in the Major Leagues
the pitcher had more on the baseball,
so much stuff that I struck out
three times in one game,
and they called him, Strike out, Casey.
And they commenced instead of saying K.C.,
they put in C.A.S.E.Y.
So then they told about
when I was going better n' better,
finally they said that
Rip Van Wrinkle went away for seventeen years,
and Runyon, I believe it was, put it in the papers,
said that, uh, Rip Van Wrinkle arrived back
in a World Series in 1921,
and when I had a bruise on my heel,
and I stumbled ball from second to third,
then from third to home,
and winnin' the game with a home run
with Bob Musil, throwin' the ball,
he sez, Rip Van Wrinkle arrived today
and played center field for the Giants,
and he was better known in the olden days
as Strike Out Casey.

DE HUNTA

Verse and pictures by John R. Dunn

EEN DE FUL VEN YECK VROST GOMMINK
   HALL DE GONS DE HUNTA GLEENINK.
SES TO VIFE, "VE QUIDT DE PUCHER."
   "YA I," SES VIFE, "KNOW VOT YOU MEANINK."

"VEET HALL DOT TOW DOT YOU PE ZPENDINK
   HON DE GONS EN HUNTINK YUNK
VE KOOT TO HUSHOLT LOAN PE LENDINK
   HOR PUY DE PUCHER ZHOP, YOU GLUNK."

"NOW NOW MUMA," SES DE NEEMRUT,
   "DUNT PE HALL DE HINSITES KET
HIN DE HUPROAR HOR YOU KOOT PE
   KETTIN ZTROKE (I HOPE) MINE PET."

EEN DE VOOTS DE MIDY HUNTA
   SHASE DE MOOZE, DE PEAR, DE TEER.
GOMMIN HUM HE DREG VON REBBET
   SES DE VIFE, "VOR DIS HI CHEER?"

DUN EEN SVAMP DE VOOT PE KEV MEN
   SOOTIN HAT DE TUCKS HALL VEEK
HUM HE'S DREGGEN VORN HOUT RIZE HAN
   SES DE VIFE, "VOT ES DOT VREAK?"

HUP VROM GRECK OF TAWN DE SOOTA
   TREMP DE GONFIELD HAN HET LEST
PESSENT YUMP HAN SCARE DE HERO
   VEN HE DRUP DE GON HIT BLEST.

HUM ES GOM DE VOOT BROVIDER
   VIFE VEELS PESSENT VIT DE HENTS
EN GIFFS TO GONQUERING HERO WERDICT,
   "TOO MUCH PE PEES HIN DE PENTS."

GOMS DE MORAL HUF DE ZTORY
   EEF YOU VANT TO HUNDT VOR REAL
YUST PEFORE DE ZEASON HOPENS
   VIT DE PUTCHER MEK DE DEAL.

New Portraits in an American Gallery

ILLUSTRATIONS RY MICHAEL LOWENBEIN

CRISPUS ATTUCKS (1723-1770)

RUNAWAY SLAVE, EX-SEAMAN, PATRIOT. One of the first Americans to die for American Freedom. Demonstrating with other colonists against British tyranny and taxation, Attucks was the first of five men to be shot down by British troops on March 5, 1770. This famous incident became the celebrated "Boston Massacre" which was authenticated by patriot, Paul Revere, who published a poem and a drawing of the historic event, in the Boston Gazette on March 12, 1770. Today Crispus Attucks' name leads the list on the monument of granite and bronze, erected to commemorate the struggle for American independence, in Boston Commons.

IRA FREDERICK ALDRIDGE (1807-1867)

TRAGEDIAN ACTOR. Born in Maryland. Studied at the African Free School in New York, Schenectady College and the University of Glasgow. Internationally acclaimed for his magnificent portrayal of Shakespeare's Othello at the Royalty Theatre in London 1826. Played Macbeth, King Lear, Shylock and other famous Shakespearean dramas in major cities and capitals throughout Europe. Recipient of the First Medal of Arts and Sciences from the King of Prussia, Cross of Leopold from the Tsar of Russia, Maltese Cross from the City of Bern. Today, there is an Ira Aldridge chair in his honor at the Shakespeare Memorial Theatre at Stratford-on-Avon.

331

FREDERICK A. DOUGLASS (1817-1895)

ABOLITIONIST AND STATESMAN. Born in slavery in Tuckahoe, Maryland. Wrote classic Narrative of an American Slave, 1845. Published North Star (later called F. Douglass Paper, 1847). Advised President Abraham Lincoln on possible role of the Negro in Civil War, (1862-1863). Elected president of Freedman's Bank and Trust Company in 1874. Appointed U.S. Marshal for District of Columbia in 1877. Appointed Minister-Resident and Consul-General to Haiti and Charge d'Affairs to Santo Domingo in 1869.

HARRIET TUBMAN (1823-1913)

CONDUCTOR OF THE UNDERGROUND RAILROAD. Born in slavery in Bucktown, Maryland. Underground Railroad was neither railroad or underground, but a system for helping countless thousands of slaves to escape to the North. From 1850 to 1857 she guided more than 300 slaves to freedom. Served as nurse in Union Army in 1862-1863. Established Harriet Tubman Home at Auburn, New York for elderly Negroes. Received medal from Queen Victoria. Buried in Ohio with military honors.

ROBERT SMALLS (1839-1915)

UNITED STATES CONGRESSMAN AND NAVAL HERO. Born in slavery in Beaufort, South Carolina. Forced to serve as a deckhand on the Planter, a Confederate transport vessel, Smalls, on May 13, 1862 in Charleston Harbor, secretly captured and piloted the Planter to the Union Navy. On December 1, 1863 Smalls was freed and made Captain of the Planter. Served out Civil War as blockading pilot for United States Navy. Elected to South Carolina State House of Representatives, 1868. Elected to South Carolina State Senate, 1870. Served three terms in United States Congress from 1875-1887.

DR. DANIEL HALE WILLIAMS (1858-1931)

NOTED SURGEON. Born in Pennsylvania. Earned M.D. degree from Chicago Medical School in 1883. Founded Provident Hospital in Chicago in 1891. Performed first successful heart operation in 1893. Reorganized Freedmen's Hospital in Washington, D.C. in 1894. Became first Negro staff physician with St. Luke and Mercy Hospital in Chicago. Affiliated with Northwestern University School of Medicine. Elected a Fellow of the American College of Surgeons, 1913.

HENRY OSSAWA TANNER (1859-1937)

PAINTER OF RELIGIOUS SUBJECTS. Born in Pittsburgh, Pennsylvania. Studied at the Pennsylvania Academy of Fine Arts and Julian Academy in Paris. Achieved honors in 1896 with famous paintings "Daniel in the Lion's Den" and "Resurrection of Lazarus" which was bought by the French government in 1897 for the Luxembourg Gallery. Awarded: French Salon Medal in 1897 and 1907, The Walter Lippincott Prize in 1900, The Louisiana Purchase Exposition Prize in 1904 and the Harris Prize from the Art Institute of Chicago in 1906.

341

GEORGE WASHINGTON CARVER (1864-1943)

AGRICULTURAL RESEARCH SCIENTIST. Born in slavery at Diamond Grove, Missouri. Master of Science degree from Iowa State College. Faculty member of Tuskegee Institute 1896. Fellow of the Royal Academy of England, 1916. Received Spingarn Medal from NAACP, 1923. Developed more than 100 different products from the sweet potato and extracted more than 300 different products from the peanut. Awarded Roosevelt Medal for distinguished service to science in 1939.

343

MATTHEW ALEXANDER HENSON (1866-1955)

EXPLORER. Born in Charley County, Maryland. Voyaged to Japan, France, Spain, West Africa, Russia and the Philippines in search of adventure. Accompanied Admiral Robert E. Peary in expeditions to reach North Pole in 1891, 1900, 1902 and 1905. April 6, 1909 Henson, sent forward by Peary, became the first man to reach the North Pole, as he planted the American Flag on the 'Top-of-the-World.' Received the Gold Medal of the Geographic Society and the Congressional Medal of Honor. (Civil Division.)

345

PAUL LAURENCE DUNBAR (1872-1906)

NATIONAL POET. Born in Dayton, Ohio. Published first volume of poems, Oak and Ivy in 1893; wrote dialect poems in Majors and Minors, 1895 and Lyrics of Lowly Life, 1896 that captured the humor and gentleness of the lives of Negroes in the rural South. Additional volumes of poems: Lyrics of Love and Laughter, Lyrics of Sunshine and Shadow, Lyrics of the Hearthside, were nationally read with his novels; The Sport of the Gods, the Uncalled, the Love of Landry and the Fanatics.

347

MARY McLEOD BETHUNE (1875-1955)

WHITE HOUSE ADVISOR, EDUCATOR. Born in Maysville, South Carolina. Graduated from Scotia Seminary in Concord, North Carolina, 1893. Founder and President of Bethune-Cookman College, Daytona, Florida, 1904. Founded National Council of Negro Women. Received Spingarn Medal from NAACP, 1935. Appointed director of Negro Affairs Division of the National Youth Administration by President Franklin D. Roosevelt, 1936. Florida State Director of the American Red Cross. Consultant to founding conference of the United Nations. Called the First Lady of the Negro Race.

DR. MARTIN LUTHER KING, A.B., Ph.D., LHD, DD, LLD (1929-1968)

CIVIL RIGHTS MOVEMENT LEADER. Born in Atlanta, Georgia. Recipient of Pearl Plafkner Award for Scholarship, 1951. Selected one of the 10 outstanding personalities of 1956. Named "Man of the Year" in 1963 by Time Magazine. Awarded Nobel Peace Prize 1964. Pastor, Dexter Avenue Baptist Church in Montgomery, Alabama. President, Southern Christian Leadership Conference. Member: NAACP, Alpha Phi Alpha, Sigma Pi Phil, Elk. Author: Stride Toward Freedom, 1958. Why We Can't Wait, 1964. His non-violent dramatic marches and speeches led to passage of Civil Rights Act in 1964. Outstanding spokesman for the Negro people. Assassinated April 4, 1968.

Now **Clancy** was a peaceful man
if you know what I mean,
The police picked up the pieces
after **Clancy** left the scene,
He never looked for trouble
that's a fact you can assume.
But nevertheless
when trouble would press,
Clancy lowered the boom!

Oh, that **Clancy,**
Oh, that **Clancy,**
Whenever they got his Irish up,
Clancy lowered the

AN OLD SONG

352

Ode to Billy Joe

A SONG BY BOBBIE GENTRY (ASCAP)

It was the third of June, another sleepy, dusty, delta day,
I was out choppin' cotton and my brother was bailin' hay;
And at dinnertime we stopped and walked back to the house to eat,
And Mama hollered at the back door, "Y'all remember to wipe your feet."
Then she said, "I got some news this mornin' from Choctaw Ridge,
Today Billy Joe McAllister jumped off the Tallahatchee Bridge."

Papa said to Mama, as he passed around the black-eyed peas,
"Well, Billy Joe never had a lick o' sense, pass the biscuits please,
There's five more acres in the lower forty I've got to plow,"
And Mama said it was a shame about Billy Joe anyhow.
Seems like nothin' ever comes to no good up on Choctaw Ridge,
And now Billy Joe McAllister's jumped off the Tallahatchee Bridge.

Brother said he recollected when he and Tom and Billy Joe,
Put a frog down my back at the Carroll County picture show,
And wasn't I talkin' to him after church last Sunday night,
I'll have another piece of apple pie, you know, it don't seem right.
I saw him at the sawmill yesterday on Choctaw Ridge,
And now you tell me Billy Joe's jumped off the Tallahatchee Bridge.

Mama said to me, "Child what's happened to your appetite?
I been cookin' all mornin' and you haven't touched a single bite,
That nice young preacher Brother Taylor dropped by today,
Said he'd be pleased to have dinner on Sunday, Oh, by the way,
He said he saw a girl that looked a lot like you up on Choctaw Ridge
And she an' Billy Joe was throwin' somethin' off the Tallahatchee Bridge."

A year has come and gone since we heard the news 'bout Billy Joe,
Brother married Becky Thompson, they bought a store in Tupelo,
There was a virus goin' 'round, Papa caught it and he died last spring,
And now Mama doesn't seem to want to do much of anything.
And me I spend a lot of time pickin' flowers up on Choctaw Ridge,
And drop them into the muddy water off the Tallahatchee Bridge.

The Buck and the Old Man

**A STORY BY JOHN R. DUNN,
WITH PAINTINGS BY TED RAND**

The buck was dead.
His great head was down between his forefeet,
the massive antlers tangled in the stunted spruce clump
just where the old man said I'd find him.
He was still warm
and I knew he had been dead
for only a few minutes.
Now I sensed the reason for my errand—
I knew the old man too was dead.
As I cut out the sack of scar tissue
containing the misshapen, expanded bullet
pressing against the buck's still warm but ruptured heart,
it was almost like touching the old man's heart,
still warm and now ruptured.

They had experienced a sort of love affair,
these two, old deer and old man,
if such a thing is possible.

It had started long ago
when the buck had just reached maturity.
He had challenged
and driven off the aging boss buck
and he had taken over the does and fawns.
The old man,
then approaching old age,
lived to hunt.
It was inevitable that these two,
sharing the same lovely forest,
would meet.
When they did,
the old man's shot was straight
but it didn't kill.
"It hit a tree," he said.
"Went through four inches of rotten wood and expanded,
before it got to him.
No blood.
I hope it didn't hurt him bad."

That night the old man had a mild heart attack.
He called it indigestion.
The human mind is strange.
I don't believe
we can ever completely understand its workings.

We were a family of woodsmen at first.
My parents had settled far from any town
in what was then virgin forest.
Other people settled in the vicinity
but neighbors were never closer than four or five miles.
I am the youngest of three sons.
My mother died bearing me.
We grew up knowing only the woods
except for sporadic attempts at education
at a typical backwoods school.
The land was unfit for farming
but wonderful white pine was there for the cutting.
At first the river, and later winter roads
provided a means of transporting the timber
to market in the south.

357

As the timber was cut,
the moose retreated and the deer moved in.
By the time I was old enough to shoot a gun,
venison was our staple diet.
I wanted no part of civilization
and finally the old man relented
and let me quit school.
He and I logged, hunted and fished,
and the old man educated me in the ways of the woods.
My brothers grew up,
went south to high school
and eventually went to college.
However, we always kept one important date:
The old man, my two brothers and I
always spent the deer-hunting season
at our home in the woods.
And the old man always said,
"Everybody, let the buck alone."

Now the buck was dead.
I wiped the blood off my hands,
cleaned my knife
and put the old man's aged bullet in my pocket.
"So long, old buck."
I was an hour from home
but I knew there was no rush now.
The old man too was dead.
"So long, old man."
I noticed that the strange breeze
that usually swirled around the spruce island
was still.

Our last hunt started out like all the others.
My brothers took stands on the main runways into the bog
and I moved the deer toward them.
The old man took off across the bog alone.
He wanted no company and we respected his wishes.
He came back that night dragging a spike buck,
but his face was ashen.
He couldn't eat or drink and we put him in bed.

My oldest brother started
for the store
at the end of the road
to call a doctor.
In the meantime,
the old man told me
what I had to do.
"The swamp buck is down and dying.
He didn't lead his bunch to safety
on the island this morning
when the shooting started.
The bullet I put in him
eight years ago
is killing him now.
Go to his trail
where he used to lose you
when you tried to track him.
Don't cross the river there
because he would track back
and go up the creek to the island.
He will be under the spruce
looking out.
There is a patch of white hair
on the scar
almost in the middle of his chest.
Cut the bullet out and bring it here."

I waited for the coroner
and we walked to the cabin together.
The doctor was there before us.
My brothers wanted to tell me
about the old man's last moments,
but I knew.
I put the bullet
in the old man's pocket
and buried it with him.

I still live in our old cabin home.
My brothers come up every deer season
and we live much as we used to.
There is another big buck on the island
and he is not afraid of me.
Every deer season I watch him herd his bunch
to safety on the island.
I stand guard over them each day of the season,
keeping all hunters away,
and I shoot my meat
from the other side of the forest.

Fly Bird

**A SONG BY DANIELLE MARTIN,
LETTERED BY RAY BARBER**

When I left home this morning
feeling sad as can be
I saw a little bird
looking at me
and I said
Fly bird
and I said
Fly bird
for you are free
oh, unlike me

The little bird was frightened
but he did not fly from me
I took him in my hand
so tenderly
and I said
Fly bird
and I said
Fly bird
for you are free
oh, unlike me

Then I discovered why he did not fly
His little wing was broken
he could not fly
His little wing was broken
he did not cry
nor will I
Although my heart is broken
I will not cry
I will learn to fly again

Stay with me little blue bird
I will mend your broken wing
and you can sing me new songs
to mend a broken heart
then we'll depart
Fly bird
for we'll be free
of broken wings
and broken hearts
we'll be free
both you and me.

From: *The People, Yes* by Carl Sandburg, picture by Henry Markowitz, photograph by Ken Kay

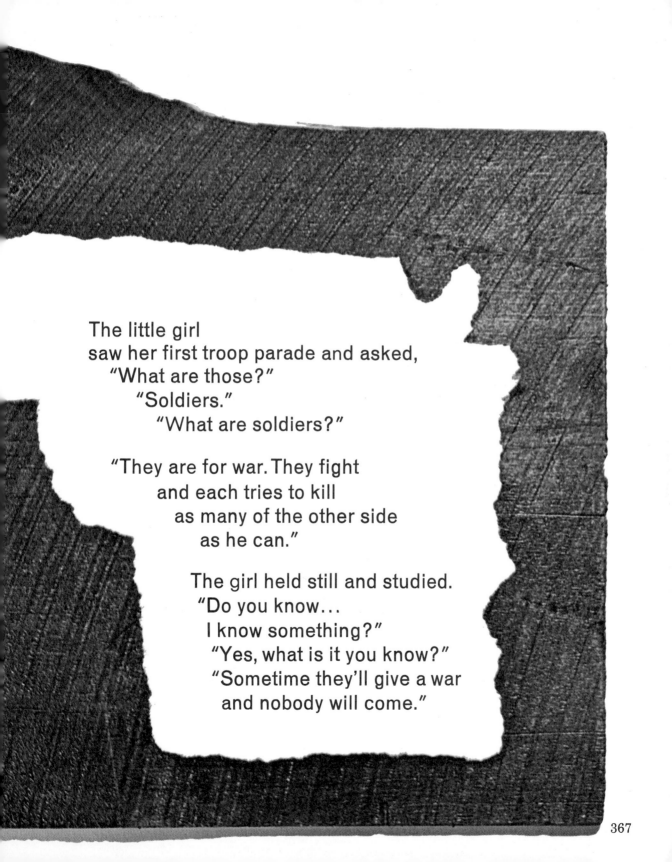

The little girl
saw her first troop parade and asked,
   "What are those?"
    "Soldiers."
      "What are soldiers?"

"They are for war. They fight
   and each tries to kill
     as many of the other side
     as he can."

    The girl held still and studied.
    "Do you know...
   I know something?"
    "Yes, what is it you know?"
    "Sometime they'll give a war
    and nobody will come."

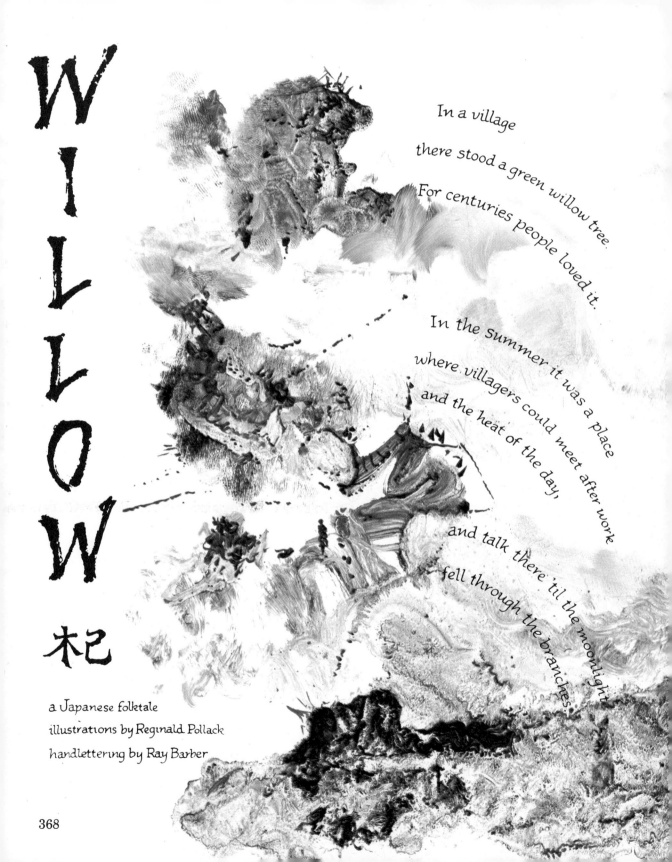

WILLOW

杞

In a village
there stood a green willow tree.
For centuries people loved it.

In the Summer it was a place
where villagers could meet after work
and the heat of the day,

and talk there 'til the moonlight
fell through the branches.

a Japanese folktale
illustrations by Reginald Pollack
handlettering by Ray Barber

368

In winter
it was a half-open umbrella
covered with snow.

A young farmer named Heitaro lived near the tree, and he,
more
than any other,
loved the huge willow.

It was the first thing he saw on waking,
and the last at sleeping.

Its shape greeted him when he returned from the fields, and all day he could see its crest. Sometimes he would burn a joss-stick beneath its branches and kneel down and pray.

One day an old man from the village came to Heitaro and explained to him that the people were anxious to build a bridge over the river, and that they particularly wanted the willow tree for timber.

"My dear willow for a bridge?"
said Heitaro, covering his face.
"Planks below feet? No!
Take my own trees first,
and spare the willow."

The villagers accepted
Heitaro's trees
and the willow stood.

371

One night while Heitaro was sitting under the tree he saw a beautiful woman close beside him. She stood and looked at him shyly, as if she wanted to speak.

"Honorable lady," said Heitaro, "I shall go home. I see you wait for somebody you love, and my presence here is uncouth."

"He will not come now," said the woman. "Has he grown cold?" said Heitaro.

"It is terrible when a mock love woos and leaves ashes."

"He has not grown cold," she said.

"And yet he does not come?" said Heitaro, "What strangeness is this?"

"He has come! His heart has always been here,

here under this willow tree."

And the woman smiled, and left him.

Night after night they met there.
The woman's shyness disappeared, and it seemed that she could not hear too much praise of the willow tree from Heitaro's lips.

One night he said to her, "Little one, will you be my wife?" "Yes," she said. "Call me Higo, and ask no questions, for love of me."

Heitaro and Higo were married,

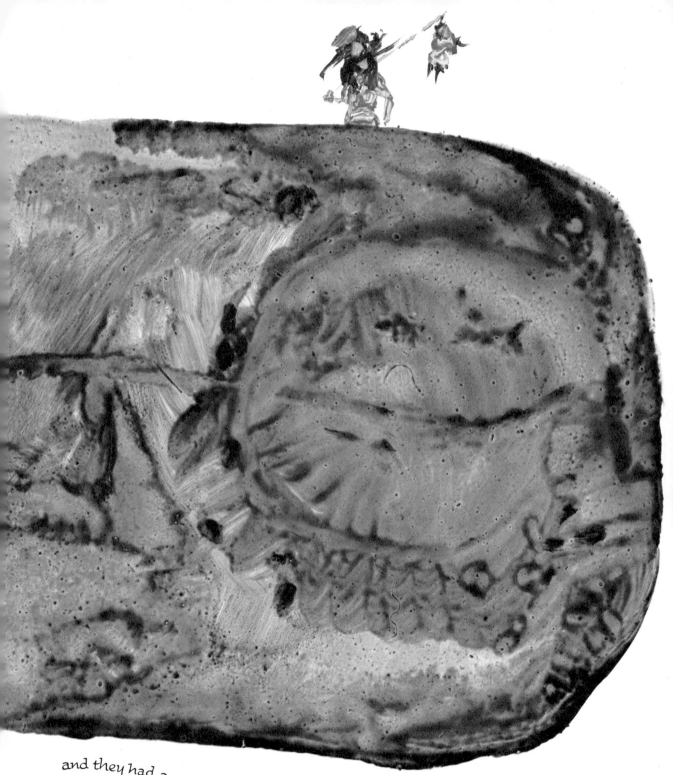

and they had a son called Chiyodo,
and they were happy.

Great news came to the village, and it was not long before Heitaro learnt of it.

The Emperor wished to build a temple in Kyoto, and his ministers were searching the land for the best timber. It would be an eternal honor to have given even a fragment of that holy shrine, and the villagers looked around them for a sacrifice that would be worthy. There was only the willow.

Heitaro offered every tree on his land, and the price of his farm, but only the willow had the quality that was sought.

"Oh, wife, my Higo,"
he said that evening.
"They are going to cut down the willow.
Before I married you
I could not have endured it.
But, having you,
perhaps I shall get over it some day."

378

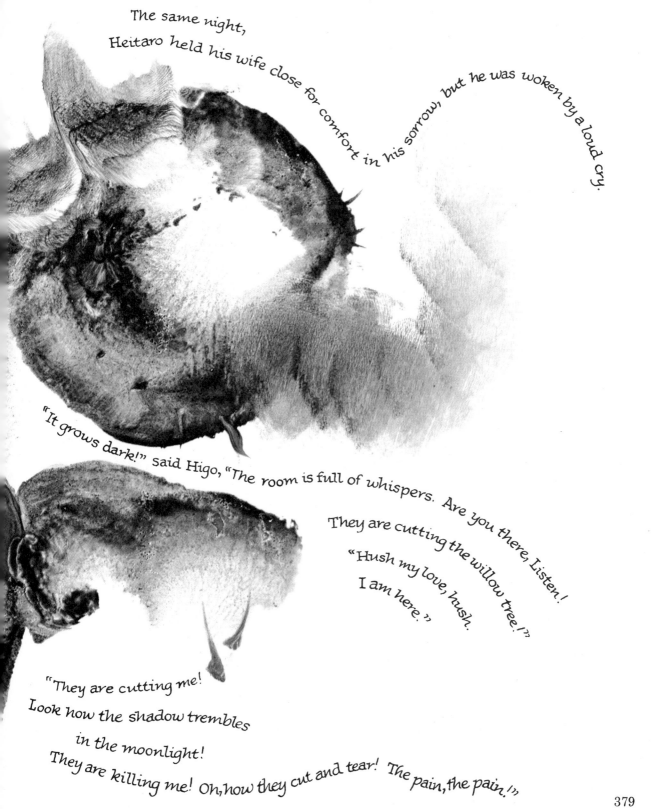

The same night,
Heitaro held his wife close for comfort in his sorrow, but he was woken by a loud cry.

"It grows dark!" said Higo, "The room is full of whispers. Are you there, Listen!

They are cutting the willow tree!"

"Hush my love, hush.
I am here."

"They are cutting me!
Look how the shadow trembles
in the moonlight!
They are killing me! Oh, how they cut and tear! The pain, the pain.!"

"Put your hand here, and here. Surely the blows cannot fall now!"

Heitavo tried to ease her pain, but nothing he did could heal her.

pressing her wet face to his, "I am going now. My body is breaking."

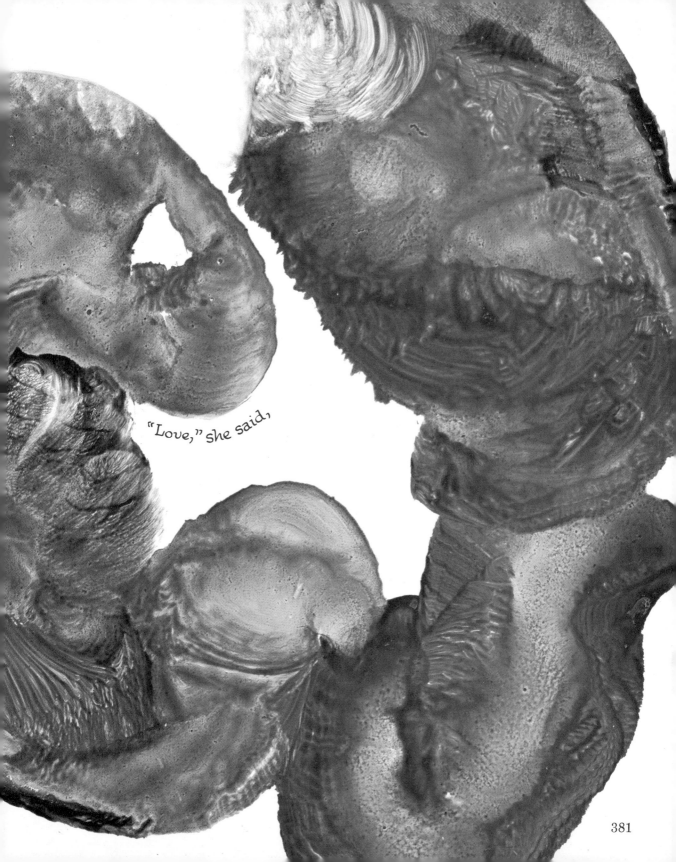

"Love," she said,

"Such a love cannot be cut down.

Heitaro!

Heitaro!

My hair is falling through the sky!"

The willow tree

lay

green and tangled

on the ground.

J'ever get the feelin' when you read the papers
    the world is cavin' in?
That the animal part of the human heart
    is fin'lly gonna win?
Well, it just may be that what you see
    are the growin' pains of liberty;

And the world ain't comin' to an end, my friend:
The world's just comin' to a start!
I feel it in my heart

The world is comin' to a start!

Ev'rybody's sayin' when you look about you
    the world is gone insane.
That the heavenly goal of the human soul
    will perish in the flame.
Well, it just may be that what they see
    is the storm before tranquility;

And the world ain't comin' to an end, my friend:
The world's just comin' to a start!
I feel it in my heart

The world is comin' to a start!

A SONG BY PETER UDELL, WITH MUSIC BY GARY GELD